Key Stage 3 Science
National Strategy Workbooks

*These books have been <u>written specifically</u> to cover the Scheme of Work.
That means they also cover the Yearly Teaching Objectives.*

Each unit in the book covers one unit from the Scheme of Work.

And there's even the odd ever-so-nearly entertaining bit, just to help keep you awake.

Contents

Contents

Published by Coordination Group Publications Ltd.

Contributors:

James Dawson

Chris Dennett

Pauline Duffield

Neil Fisher

Paddy Gannon

Dominic Hall

Jason Howell

Philippa Hulme

Simon Little

Becky May

Adriana McGarvey

Joanne Morgan

Alison Palin

Katherine Reed

Glenn Rogers

Julie Schofield

Phil Taylor

Lisa Thomas

Claire Thompson

James Paul Wallis

Chrissy Williams

Jim Wilson

With Thanks to:
Gemma Hallam, David Worthington and
Eileen Worthington for the proof reading.

ISBN 1 84146 246 2

Groovy website: www.cgpbooks.co.uk

Printed by Elanders Hindson, Newcastle upon Tyne.

Animal and Plant Organs

Q1 Name the parts of the human body labelled a) to e). Choose from the organs in the grey box.

| heart brain liver kidneys lungs |

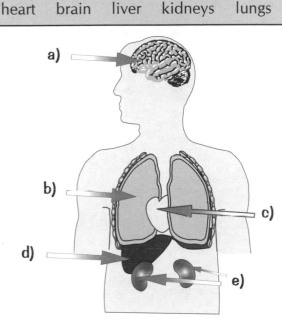

Q2 Name the parts of the plant labelled a) to d). Choose from the parts in the grey box.

| flower leaf roots stem |

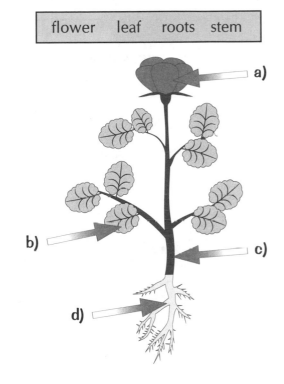

Q3 What do your organs do? Write out each of the descriptions below followed by the name of the organ being described. Choose from the organs in the box.

a) Pumps blood around the body.

b) Controls the body.

c) Clean the blood and make urine.

d) Get oxygen into the body.

e) Absorbs digested food.

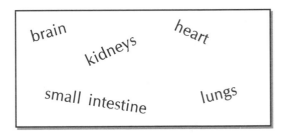

brain   kidneys   heart   small intestine   lungs

Q4 What are the main parts of a plant? Write out each of the descriptions below followed by the name of the part being described. Choose from the parts in the box.

a) They are green, flat and thin, and they make food.

b) Contains the sexual organs of the plant.

c) Tiny hairs that absorb water and minerals from the soil.

d) Holds the plant upright.

e) Holds the plant in the soil, especially when windy.

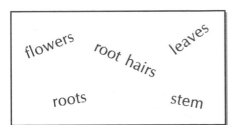

flowers   root hairs   leaves   roots   stem

Microscopes

Q1   Match the labels on this picture to the descriptions i) to iv).
Write your answer like this: A = i), B = ii) etc.

i)   EYEPIECE: the bit you look through.

ii)   STAGE: where you put the slide.

iii)   The focusing knob.

iv)   The mirror that reflects light
up into the microscope.

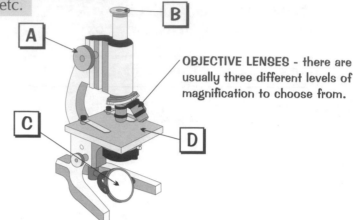

OBJECTIVE LENSES - there are
usually three different levels of
magnification to choose from.

Q2   James wants to look at a piece of onion epidermis through a microscope.
This is the equipment he has. Describe how James should prepare the slide.

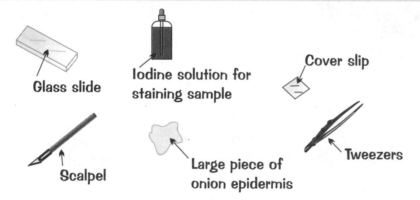

Glass slide

Iodine solution for
staining sample

Cover slip

Scalpel

Large piece of
onion epidermis

Tweezers

Q3   Write these instructions in the correct order to say how to focus the microscope on a slide.

1   Move round the three objective lenses to select the level of magnification.

2   Check the slide is in the centre of the stage.

4   Look down the microscope.

3   Adjust the mirror so that light shines up the microscope.

5   Clip the slide onto the stage so it doesn't move around.

6   Adjust the brightness.

7   Put the slide on the stage.

8   Adjust the focus to get a sharp image.

Wow, this page is surely the best in the book so far...

I reckon playing with microscopes was the most fun I ever had in a Science lesson.
(Apart from passing notes to Wilma Braithwaite...) Things can look real different up close. Like, er, bigger.

Plant and Animal Cells

Q1 Answer these questions about what animal and plant cells do.

a) Name part of an animal cell that controls the cell's activities.

b) Which part of an animal cell is the thin layer on the outside?

c) What is the name of the liquid inside an animal cell?

d) Which part of a plant cell is like a rigid box on the outside?

e) What are the little green structures found in some plant cells called?

f) Plant cells often have a large, liquid-filled space. What is it called?

Q2 For each statement, write down whether it's "true" or "false".

a) Almost all cells have a nucleus.

b) All plant cells contain chloroplasts.

c) The cell membrane controls what goes in and out of the cell.

d) Animal cells have cell membranes.

e) Animal cells have cell walls.

f) All cells contain some cytoplasm.

Q3 Copy out this table putting a tick or cross in each box
to say whether the part is found in an animal or plant cell.

Part	Nucleus	Cell Membrane	Cell Wall	Chloroplasts
Animal				
Plant				

Q4 Match up the first part of each sentence (A, B, C or D) with the second
part of each sentence (1, 2, 3 or 4) and then write out the sentences.

A The Nucleus is the part of the cell that	1. found in cells.
B Chloroplasts are green structures that	2. controls what enters and leaves the cell.
C Cytoplasm is the living liquid	3. controls what happens in the cell.
D The cell membrane	4. absorb the light energy from the sun.

Cell Function

Cells are said to be specialised if they have a particular job to do. Five examples of specialised cells are the sperm cell, the ovum, the palisade cell, the cilia cell and the root hair cell. Each has its own special job and a structure that helps it to do its job.

Q1 The sperm cell

a) Why does it have a tail?

b) Why does it have enzymes in its head?

c) What important structures are found inside the nucleus?

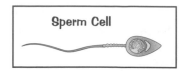
Sperm Cell

Q2 The ovum (egg cell)

a) How big is the ovum compared to most human cells?

b) What does the yolk provide to the fertilised egg?

Ovum

Q3 The palisade cell

a) Which gas is absorbed by this cell?

b) Which form of energy is absorbed by this cell?

c) Which green structures are found in large numbers here?

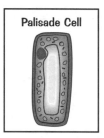
Palisade Cell

Q4 The cilia cell

a) What do the tiny hairs do to the air you breathe?

b) What is the proper name for snot?

c) What two things are trapped and swallowed at the back of the throat by these cells?

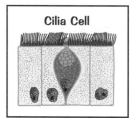
Cilia Cell

Q5 The root hair cell

a) How does the surface area of a root hair cell compare with the surface area of a normal cell?

b) What two things are absorbed by the root hair cell?

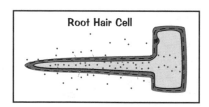
Root Hair Cell

Q6 Write down the names from the left of the table followed by the correct description from the right.

1. Tissue	A. A group of organs carrying out a common function (job)
2. Organ	B. A group of different tissues working together to carry out a common job
3. Organ System	C. A group of similar cells carrying out the same job

Q7 Match each name on the left of the chart with the correct example from the right of the chart. Give your answer as numbers and letters, eg 4 = D.

1. Tissue	A. Digestive
2. Organ	B. Muscle
3. Organ system	C. Heart

Making New Cells

There are two ways of making new cells.

1. When living things grow, new cells are made from old cells by making copies.

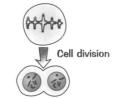

Cell division

2. When living things reproduce sexually, new cells are made by the joining together of special half-cells called gametes.

Gametes   Egg

Sperm   +   →   Fertilised egg

Q1   For each statement, write down whether it's "true" or "false"?

a) When living things grow their cells divide.

b) When living things grow the cells get smaller.

c) When living things grow the nucleus of the cell is not involved.

d) When living things grow they need energy to power the process.

e) When living things grow this usually involves cells dividing and then increasing in size.

Q2   Copy out the following sentences filling in the blanks with the correct words from the box.

fertilisation	half set	nucleus	pollination	seed	specialised

a) A pollen grain contains a .... with a half set of information about the next generation.

b) The transfer of pollen grains from the anther of one plant to the stigma of another is known as cross- ....

c) The ovule has a nucleus that contains a .... of information about the next generation.

d) The pollen and the ovule are .... cells, meaning they have a job to do and a structure to help to do it.

e) .... is the joining together of the nuclei of the pollen grain and the ovum.

f) After fertilisation, the newly produced cell grows by rapid cell division to form the ....

Q3   Write out the start of each statement on the left with the correct ending from the right.

1. Growth results in	A. involves the copying of genetic material
2. Normal cell division	B. involves the manufacture of special cells with half the genetic information of normal cells plus a cute little tail
3. New skin cells are produced by	C. the division of existing skin cells
4. Cell division starts with	D. an increase in mass
5. Sperm cell production	E. the nucleus dividing

Pollen Tubes

Q1 Write out each description below followed by the labelled part of the plant it's describing.

a) Is carried there by the wind or an insect.

b) Joins together with the male nucleus.

c) Is the structure going down the style through which the male nucleus travels.

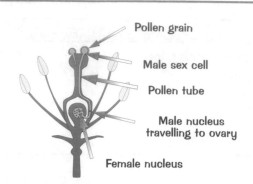

Pollen grain

Male sex cell

Pollen tube

Male nucleus travelling to ovary

Female nucleus

Q2 Fred and Freda decide to do an experiment to "find out the best sugar concentration for getting daffodil pollen tubes to grow".

a) Write out the first half of each sentence from the left of the table with the correct ending from the right, to describe the experiment.

1. Freda collects from a very healthy flower a large number of	A. temperature of 28°C.
2. Fred adds 3 drops of each sugar solution onto a labelled	B. graph of the data and ponder it carefully.
3. They then add exactly 20 pollen grains to	C. pollen grains sprout in different sugar concentrations.
4. They then cover each slide with a	D. pollen grains to use in the experiment.
5. They then leave the slides for 30 minutes in an incubator set at a constant	E. count how many pollen grains have sprouted out of the twenty.
6. They then take each slide out quickly and	F. cavity microscope slide.
7. They then have some data on how well	G. each labelled cavity slide.
8. Fred says I think we should draw a	H. coverslip.

b) Why did all the pollen grains come from the same healthy plant?

c) Why were at least twenty pollen grains needed for each sugar concentration?

d) Why were all the slides kept at a constant temperature?

Q3 Fred and Freda decided to try to find out the best temperature for sprouting of pollen grains in the daffodil. They did a similar experiment. Which of the following would have to be kept the same during the experiment? Tick yes or no for each variable.

	Yes	No
A. The number of pollen grains on each slide		
B. The temperature of all the slides in the experiment		
C. The sugar concentration on each slide		
D. The type of flower the pollen grains came from		

The Pollen Tubes — a great name for a band...

As fascinating as daffodil pollen tube growth is, the important bit of questions 2 and 3 is really understanding how the experiments are done. E.g. always make sure you have a large <u>sample size</u> (no. of grains in this case) and keep everything the same apart from the thing you're investigating.

Reproduction in Different Animals

Q1   **Copy** and **complete** the sentences by choosing the correct words from inside the brackets:

a) A new life starts when a sperm joins with an egg. This is called [fertilisation / ovulation].

b) When eggs are fertilised inside the body it's called [external / internal] fertilisation.

Q2   Study this table and answer the questions below:

Animal	Average No. Eggs Produced	Where Eggs are Laid
Salmon	Thousands	Water
Green Sea Turtles	115	Sand
Golden Eagle	2	Land

a) Which of the animals above
carries out external fertilisation?

b) Give two reasons why fish lay so many eggs.

c) Why do Golden Eagles lay fewer eggs than turtles?

Q3   The following statements describe mammals. Some are true and some are false.
Copy them out under the headings true and false.

a) Mammals only ever reproduce on land.

b) Mammalian young are fertilised internally and develop in the uterus.

c) Mammals produce milk to feed the young after birth.

d) Mammals abandon their young immediately after birth.

e) Mammals cannot walk until they are at least one year old.

f) Mammals give birth to live young.

Q4   A newborn gazelle (a small breed of antelope that feeds on grass and is hunted by lions) born
on the African Savannah can usually walk and see within an hour. The sight of human babies
develops over the first few months and they don't start walking until several months old.

a) Which is the more dependent on its mother, the human or the gazelle?

b) State one way in which both newborns are dependent on their mothers.

c) Why is it important that a newborn gazelle can see and walk very soon after birth?

Human Reproductive Organs

Q1 For a new life to be created a male sex cell (sperm) and a female sex cell (egg) must fuse together. The reproductive systems of men and women have different parts to play in this. This is why they have some very important differences.

a) Copy out the table and then fill in the name of each part using the diagrams on the right.

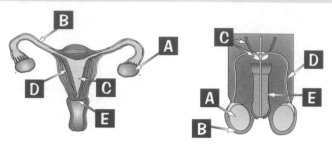

Female	Name	Male	Name
A		A	
B		B	
C		C	
D		D	
E		E	

b) Circle the names of the parts in the table that produce sex cells.

Q2 Answer the following questions:

a) Where are sperms made?

b) List the parts the sperm pass through in order to leave the man's body.

c) Where in the woman's body are the sperm deposited?

d) Why are so many sperm produced at a time?

e) Where are eggs made?

f) Where must the egg and sperm meet if fertilisation is to be successful?

g) What happens in the uterus after fertilisation has taken place?

Q3 These diagrams are in the wrong order. Copy them out in the correct order.

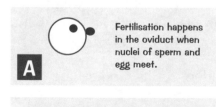

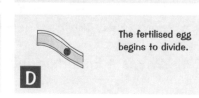

A Fertilisation happens in the oviduct when nuclei of sperm and egg meet.

B The ball of developing cells implants in the uterus.

C Ovulation — an egg is released from the ovary into the oviduct.

D The fertilised egg begins to divide.

Sperm and Egg Cells

Q1 Copy the diagrams of the sperm and egg cells, adding labels from the list below (some words will be left over):

Nucleus   Tail   Cytoplasm   Cell Wall

Cell membrane   Vacuole   Head

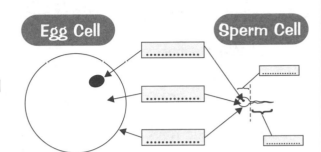

Q2 The following words are matched up with the wrong descriptions. Match them up correctly.

Egg ⟶ Contains genetic instructions.

Nucleus ⟶ Surrounds both the sperm and egg cells.

Cytoplasm ⟶ Is streamlined and small in size.

Sperm ⟶ Is an enlarged cell with food reserves.

Cell membrane ⟶ A jelly like substance that surrounds the nucleus.

Q3 Copy and complete:

For fertilisation to happen, the _ _ _ c _ _ _ _ of the male and female _ _ _ cells must

f _ s _ (join) together. This is the same in both internal and _ _ _ _ _ _ a _ fertilisation.

The sperm and the egg each contain half the _ _ _ _ _ _ _ information needed to create

a new individual. Each individual will be different, unless they are

_ _ _ n _ _ _ _ _ _ _ i _ _ . In sexual reproduction offspring will be similar to both

p _ _ _ _ _ _ , but can never be identical to them.

Q4 Sometimes more than one egg is released during ovulation or a fertilised egg can split into two. This leads to twins being produced. Copy and complete the table below by placing a tick in the boxes where the statements are correct for that type of twin.

	Identical Twins	Non-identical Twins
Share the same genetic instructions		
Their genetic instructions vary		
Are produced from one egg and one sperm		
Are produced from two eggs and two sperms		
Must be the same sex		
Can be different sexes		
Must be different sexes		

The Menstrual Cycle

Q1 Study the following diagram of the menstrual cycle then answer the questions:

a) What is happening on day one of the menstrual cycle?

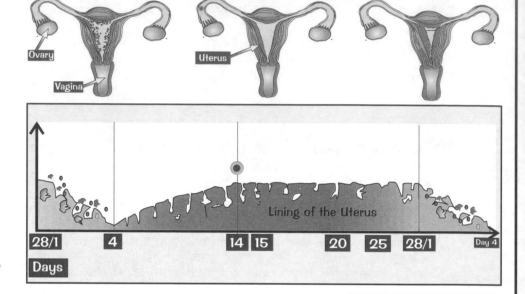

b) Between days 4 and 14 the lining of the uterus builds up. Why does it do this?

c) How many days after the start of menstruation is an egg usually released?

Key
■ = blood and lining
⊙ = egg released from ovary

d) Where is the egg released from and where does fertilisation happen?

e) Between which days is the full lining of the uterus maintained?

f) Explain what will happen to the lining of the uterus if implantation of a fertilised egg cell occurs.

g) If a woman started menstruating on the 2nd January, on what date is her next period due?

Q2 Rearrange the jumbled up letters to find the correct words:

a) The breaking down of the uterus lining which results in blood loss is **MRSTANEUTION**.

b) The changes that happen to the female reproductive system over 28 days is called the **SLAURMENT CLYCE**.

c) The lining of the uterus grows in preparation for **ATLIMPNATION**.

d) The release of the egg cell from the ovary is **OVALUTION**.

e) If fertilisation and implantation happens the embryo will develop in the **RESTUU**.

"The wrong time of the month" is much easier to pronounce...

There are quite a few fancy names to learn here. Practise by drawing diagrams of the sex organs (sciencey diagrams, remember) and labelling all the bits with the right (science) names.

Pregnancy

Q1 If a woman's period is late then she may be pregnant.
She can take a test that detects chemicals in her urine to confirm this.
Replace the letters in the table with the correct words from the grey box.

Zygote

Ovum

Embryo

Fetus

Name	Description
A	The fertilised egg.
B	Developing in the uterus. Limbs are not yet present.
C	The eyes and limbs have formed. The heart is beating.

Q2 Below is a diagram of a developing fetus.

a) Copy and complete the table with the name and function for each letter on the diagram.

b) If a woman is pregnant, will she continue having periods? Explain your answer.

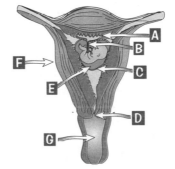

	Name	Function
A		
B		
C		
D		
E		
F		
G		

c) What other changes may happen to her body that would suggest she was pregnant?

d) How many babies is she most likely to produce from one pregnancy?

Q3 Pregnant women need to stay healthy, because many substances are passed on to the fetus through the placenta and umbilical cord. For each statement, write whether it's "true" or "false".

a) Oxygen is needed, it passes from the mother to the fetus.

b) Harmful viruses such as HIV and rubella cannot be passed on to the fetus during pregnancy.

c) Water and digested food is passed from the fetus to the mother.

d) The blood of the mother and fetus do not mix in the placenta.

e) Carbon dioxide is one of the waste products made by the fetus.

f) Alcohol can pass from mother to fetus but cannot harm the fetus.

g) A pregnant woman should not smoke at any time during pregnancy as it may have a harmful effect on the development of her unborn child.

Birth

Q1   Complete the following paragraphs using the words below:

cervix	head	afterbirth	amniotic	nine
	vagina	blood	uterus	umbilical cord
closer	cushioned	birth	contractions	stronger

After .... months of pregnancy the .... of the baby is due.

The mother will experience .... , which signal the oncoming birth of her child.

This is the .... wall preparing to squeeze the baby out.

The amnion tears and the .... fluid that has protected and .... the

fetus is released through the vagina (the 'waters' break). In order for the baby to be

passed out through the vagina the .... muscle must relax (dilate).

The contractions will become .... and .... together as the mother

pushes the baby out through the .... and then out of her body. The baby

usually emerges .... first.

The .... is cut, taking care not to allow the .... of the mother and

baby to mix. The placenta must now be delivered. This is called the ....

Q2   When a baby is born it has important reflex reactions. If you touch its cheek it will turn
its head and display a sucking action. This ensures that a newborn receives nourishment.
The mother produces milk from her mammary glands after the birth of her baby.

a) List the advantages of mother's breast milk over
   non-breast milk (such as cows' milk or powdered milk).

b) Other than nutrition, in what other ways is a newborn
   baby dependent on its mother?

It's not quite as simple as "the stork brought you here" is it...

OK, to summarise this birth lark: pregnancy (9 months) — contractions — waters break — more
contractions — cervix muscle relaxes — fetus to vagina — baby out (head-first) — cut cord.

Growing Up

Q1 Study the diagrams of human development below and name each of the four stages.

a ah. bisto...

Depends on its parents in order to survive.

b

Becoming more independent. Able to walk and talk.

c

The onset of puberty signals this period of development.

d

The body is now fully developed.

Q2 One way of looking at development is by measuring height. All children develop at a different rate but this question looks at average (mean) height.

a) Using the information in the table plot a graph of male and female height. Put both lines on the same axes.

Age (years)	Male Height (cm)	Female Height (cm)
2	87	90
4	100	104
6	113	117
8	125	131
10	137	144
12	145	159
14	162	170
16	172	172
18	174	173
20	176	173

b) Between which ages do boys increase in height most rapidly?

c) Between which ages do girls increase in height most rapidly?

d) At which age is the mean height of boys and girls the same?

e) Describe how the height differences between boys and girls change as they get older.

Growing Up

Q1   Rearrange the letters to discover some more ways that growth and development can be measured.

the wig

he is daze

sad hp nan

so zit foe

Q2   For growth to happen cells must divide. Copy out the following sentences choosing the correct words from the brackets each time.

a) In order to produce new cells for growth a parent cell divides into [two / four].

b) The cells produced are [similar / identical] to the parent cell.

c) As well as growth, this also happens in the repair of cells such as [skin / sperm] cells.

Q3   A class of 28 pupils measured the height of every pupil. They produced the following graph from the data they collected.

a) What is the mode height range for this class?

b) Is the number of pupils included in this survey a big enough sample size to work out the average height for year 7 pupils in the whole of the country?

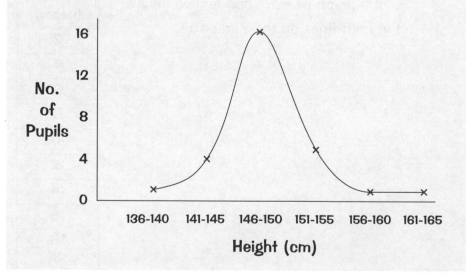

c) The tallest pupil in the class was 163 cm tall and the shortest was 136 cm tall. What is their height difference?

d) What factors can cause such differences in height between pupils of the same age?

There's no such thing as an average person...

Your height and build depend on loads of things — whether you're male or female, how fast you grow, your diet, what your parents look like, etc. It's no big deal — everyone's different, that's all.

Environmental Influences on Habitats

Q1 Copy out the sentences below choosing words from the box.
You need to use one word twice.

| adapted | environment | habitat |

a) The place where a living thing lives is called its ....

b) The conditions there make up its ....

c) Animals and plants have special features to help them survive where they live.
   You say they are .... to their environment.

d) A polar bear is well .... to its chilly environment.

Q2 Copy out the words below and draw lines to match each animal or plant to its habitat.

Jellyfish    **Seaweed**    **Camel**    **Cactus**    **Mole**

underground
tunnels   desert   open sea   on rocks
                                                 by the sea

Q3 The diagram below is all jumbled up. Write out the name of
each organism followed by where it lives and why it lives there.

LIVING THING:	FOUND WHERE:	WHY:
 Polar bear	In a cave during the day	Because it is adapted to hot, dry conditions
 Bat	In the desert	It is hunting for prey (e.g. seals and fish)
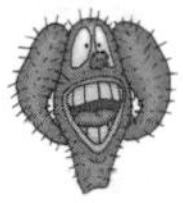 Cactus	Swimming in icy cold water	It is resting

Q4 Write down three features that are adaptations to help a badger
to feed at night in woodland. Choose from the list below.

A Large flat leaves

B Large claws for rooting around

C Ability to flap wings very quickly

D A long pointed nose for sucking up ants

E Dark coloration, mainly for camouflage

F Very sensitive hearing

Changing Environments

Q1   For each living thing, write down the feature that helps it survive in a changing environment:

Living thing:	Feature that helps it to survive:
A Swallow	1. hibernates to survive over the winter
B Butterfly	2. stores nuts underground
C Tortoise	3. spends the winter as a pupa
D Squirrel	4. grows a thick coat & stores extra fat for the winter
E Grizzly Bear	5. migrates to warmer places for the winter

Q2   For each instrument below, write down the environmental factor that it measures.

Measuring Instrument:	What does it measure?
A Thermometer	1. Noise levels
B Light Probe	2. Rainfall levels
C Rain Gauge	3. Light intensity
D Meter measuring in decibels	4. Temperature

Q3   Complete the sentences below about daily changes in plants and animals using these words:

night   nocturnal   petals   predators   salty

a) Most flowers open up their .... to allow pollination.

b) Most flowers close up their petals at .... for protection.

c) Animals that are active at night are said to be ....

d) Some animals are active at night to avoid being 'got' by ....

e) If you are a shrimp living in an estuary (where a river meets the sea) then you will have daily changes in how .... the water is.

Q4   There are four yearly changes that organisms have to adapt to.
Work out what they are, and write them out in full.

    1. t.......rat.....e   2. s.....nli.....t   3. availability of w..........   4. availability of ...oo...

Changing Environments

Q1   The table below describes what is happening over a period of 24 hours.
Copy and complete the table using the words in this box.

| Bats wake up and fly out of their roosts | Dark | First light |
| It is still light | Nocturnal animals active | Plants photosynthesising fastest |

Time	Light Level	What's happening?
Midnight		It's 12 hours after noon.
4 am	dark	
7 am		Nocturnal animals are now hidden away.
12 noon	bright light	
4 pm		Plant photosynthesis is slowing down.
8 pm	light fading	

Q2   James is conducting an experiment
to see if maggots prefer light or dark.
He puts twenty maggots in a clear round box which
has been completely covered with black paper
around one side and is stood on white paper on the
other side and has a lamp shining on it.

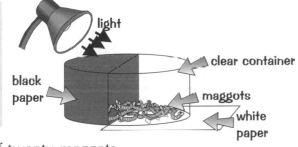

a) Is a sample of twenty maggots
large enough for an investigation?

b) What do maggots prefer — light or dark?

c) When in the experiment do you think they started
to show a clear choice between light and dark?

d) Why would a further experiment with three different
batches of twenty maggots give more reliable results?

e) What else might affect maggot
behaviour in this experiment?

f) Why do you think maggots prefer what they do?
(Hint: think about predators)

Time (minutes)	Number on the dark side	Number on the light side
Start (maggots dropped in box)	9	11
0.5	12	8
1	17	3
1.5	10	10
2	11	9
2.5	15	5
3	17	3
3.5	15	5
4	18	2
4.5	17	3
5	19	1

Maggot experiments — that James is a bit weird if you ask me...

All environments change on a daily basis. Plants and animals need to adapt to these changes.
Animals come out at different times of day when they have the best chance of finding food without
being eaten. And plants do clever things like closing their petals at night — well it's clever for a plant.

Feeding Relationships

Q1   Write down each sentence and say if it describes a **predator** or **prey**.

   A   an animal that hunts and kills for its food

   B   an animal that is hunted and killed as food for another animal

Q2   Copy the table and for each animal, tick the column it's most likely to belong to.

Animal	Predator	Prey
Lion		
Rabbit		
Earthworm		
Eagle		

Q3   Copy the table and decide whether each feature belongs to a predator or prey. Put a tick in the appropriate column. (Some features will apply to both.)

Feature	Predator	Prey
Sharp claws		
Eyes on the side of the head for all round vision		
Excellent hearing and sense of smell		
Excellent camouflage		
Eyes forward		

Q4   Copy and complete these sentences using words from the box. You need to use one word twice.

> carnivore   herbivore   omnivore   producer   vegetarian

   a) A living thing that manufactures its own food is called a ....

   b) A living thing that eats only plant material is a ....

   c) A living thing that eats only other animals is a ....

   d) A living thing that eats both plants and animals is an ....

   e) A person who never eats meat is both a .... and a ....

Q5   Copy each sentence below and say if it describes a **food chain** or a **food web**.

   A A diagram of a single set of living things showing what is eaten by what.

   B A more complex diagram showing how living things may be interlinked by the many different living things they eat.

Food Chains

Q1   Each food chain is jumbled up. Write each one out in the correct order.

a) Fiona (the vegetarian) → lettuce

b) Phil (a human) → grass → Daisy the cow

c) Seeds → Oscar the Siamese cat → small bird

d) Chicken → corn → Sylvia (a human)

e) Jean (a nice Frenchman) → French lettuce → large juicy French snails

f) Pond snail → pond plant → fish → Fred the fisherman

g) Whale → tiny plankton → squid

h) Large top carnivore bird → oak leaves → robin → juicy caterpillar

i) Hawk → leaves → ladybirds → greenfly → blue-tits

j) Animal plankton → plant plankton → whale → krill (little Arctic shrimp-type creatures)

Q2   Use this food chain to answer the questions below.

Pond weed   Tadpole   Water beetle   Pike

a)   What does the arrow between each living thing mean?

b)   What actually passes down the food chain — **energy** or **Emma B**?

c)   What usually happens to the numbers of living things as you go down the chain?

d)   What usually happens to the size of the living things as you go down the chain?

e)   Name the producer in this food chain.

f)   Name the primary consumer in this food chain.

g)   Name the secondary consumer in this food chain.

h)   Name the tertiary consumer in this food chain.

i)   Name the herbivore in this food chain.

j)   Name two carnivores in this food chain.

k)   Name the top carnivore in this food chain.

l)   Name two predators in this food chain

m)   Name two living things in the food chain that are prey to predators.

Lion ⟹ Rabbit??
I wished I'd listened more ...
this can't be right

Unit 7C — Environment and Feeding Relationships

Food Webs

Q1 For each of the observations A, B and C, pick a possible conclusion from the second column. Write your answers as e.g. "D=6".

Evidence from observations (what you see)	Possible Conclusion (what you decide)
A Greenfly found on Rosebush	1. Spiders do not eat woodlice
B Woodlice found under a decaying log	2. Spiders trap and eat houseflies
C Housefly trapped in a spider's web	3. Greenfly feed on roses
	4. Woodlice feed on rotting wood
	5. Woodlice are eaten by spiders

Q2 The diagram below shows a food web.

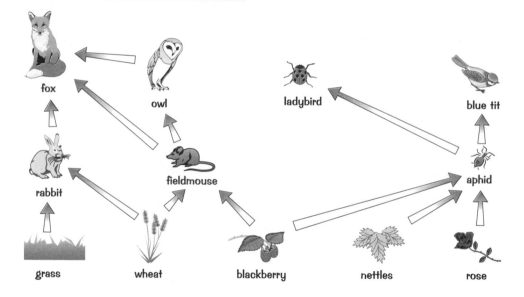

a) Name all of the producers.

b) What type of living things are all of the producers?

c) Name all of the primary consumers.

d) Name all of the secondary consumers.

e) How many tertiary consumers are shown?

What would happen if..........

f) All the blue tits suddenly died?

g) All of the ladybirds vanished?

h) All of the rabbits were killed by a nasty disease called myxomatosis?

i) All the baby owls failed to hatch this year?

Food Webs

Q1   Are the following statements about food webs "true" or "false"?

   a) Food webs try to show more information about what eats what than food chains.

   b) What passes through the web in the direction of the arrows is energy.

   c) Energy flows in the web from secondary consumer to primary consumer to producer.

   d) At the opposite end of the chain to the producers we find animals called top carnivores.

Q2   Try this fantastic 'Food Webs Crossword'. Write the answers in your book.

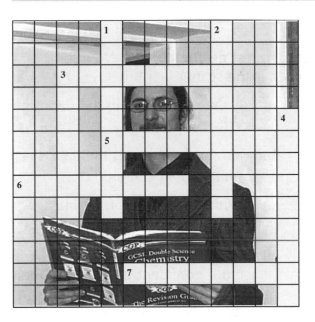

Clues Across

   3. It uses the sun's energy to produce food containing chemical energy (8)

   5. An animal which eats only plants, such as a rabbit (9)

   6. This animal is the type of consumer that eats secondary consumers (8)

   7. Plants are producers but each animal is a .... (8)

Clues Down

   1. A simple diagram to show what eats what and in what sequence (4,5)

   2. An animal that eats only animals, never plants (9)

   3. This type of consumer eats producers (7)

   4. This type of consumer eats primary consumers (9)

Q3   Look at the 'Food Webs Wordsearch' below. See how quickly you can find the key words in the grid. Draw your own 15 × 11 grid to put your answers in.

Carnivore	Herbivore
Consumer	Omnivore
Energy	Primary
Food chain	Secondary
Food web	Tertiary

S	E	C	O	N	D	A	R	Y	H	M	U	B	S	A
F	R	R	B	I	Z	P	E	H	L	U	J	V	D	Y
O	O	V	O	T	Q	D	C	O	N	S	U	M	E	R
O	V	O	X	V	M	W	U	C	Y	X	O	T	R	A
D	I	M	D	F	I	D	D	K	Q	G	N	Q	L	M
W	N	N	R	C	A	B	O	Q	R	I	R	L	I	I
E	R	I	R	K	H	Y	R	A	I	T	R	E	T	R
B	A	V	U	P	A	A	P	E	H	O	Y	P	N	P
J	C	O	N	A	Z	Z	I	B	H	G	Y	J	Y	E
V	R	R	M	I	H	Z	R	N	Y	I	B	Y	I	K
D	W	E	U	L	A	F	I	U	C	Q	V	A	I	H

Wow, what a really SPECIAL page...

Do you recognise the man hiding in the crossword and wordsearch? That's right, it's Jumbo Wilson. That's why this page is so special. Take a moment to savour the beauty of this page before moving on.

Differences in Species

Q1   Sarah records the shoe size of every person in her class on the bar chart below.

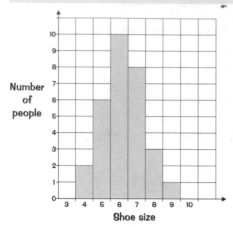

a)   What is the smallest shoe size in the class?

b)   What is the most common shoe size?

c)   How many people are in her class?

d)   How many people are there in the class whose feet are size 6 or over?

Q2   Joel says "the tallest people have the longest feet." To test his theory he measures 10 members of his class (labelled A to J) and produces the scatter graph below.

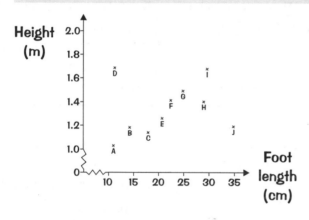

a)   Is there a pattern in the data? What is it?

b)   How strongly does the data support Joel's theory?

c)   Which members of the class do not fit the pattern? Describe them.

d)   What should Joel do to be more confident in his conclusion?

Q3   Peter suggests that "the tallest people have the longest hair."

He tests the whole class and plots the scatter graph opposite.

Does the data collected support Peter's idea?

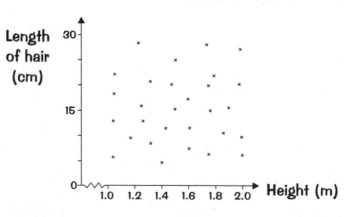

Q4   Beth thinks that longer holly leaves have more prickles.
She collects data from 10 holly leaves and puts them in a table.

Holly leaf	1	2	3	4	5	6	7	8	9	10
Length (cm)	6	10	7	8	8	9	5	4	10	7
Prickles	5	9	6	9	11	8	5	4	10	7

a)   Plot a scatter graph of length against number of prickles.

b)   Does the data support Beth's idea?

The Causes of Variation

Q1   Copy and complete the paragraph below. Use the words from the grey box.

> ENVIRONMENTAL   HEIGHT   DIFFERENT
>
> INHERIT   LIGHT   WATER   COLOUR OF PETALS

Individuals of the same species are all slightly ....

Variation in characteristics can be caused by genes that we ....

from our parents. Variation can also be caused by .... factors.

An example of an inherited characteristic for a rose could be ....

Variation in a characteristic such as .... could be caused by

lack of .... or ....

Q2   A family is shown below.

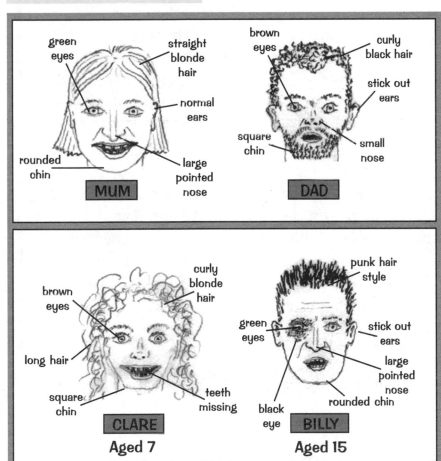

a)   List the features that Billy has inherited from

   i) his mother

   ii) his father

b)   List the features that Clare has inherited from

   i) her mother

   ii) her father

c)   List the children's features which are due to environmental factors.

d)   Will Billy inherit his father's beard?

   Explain your answer.

Don't blame me, I didn't draw them...

Thanks to inherited features and environmental factors we're all different.
That's just as well, imagine if we were all the same — variety is the spice of life.

Describing Living Things

Read the descriptions of these imaginary animals carefully, then answer the questions.

Animal A

This animal is about 2m long and covered in thick fur. Once it finds a mate it stays with the same partner for life. It gives birth to live young and feeds its offspring milk for their first year. It has long horns and four legs. When it moves it tends to bounce on its hind legs. It has large eyes but usually relies on its excellent sense of hearing to warn of danger. It eats most plants and has large rear teeth for chewing. In the winter it hibernates in its cave having stored a lot of energy as fat.

Animal B

This animal lives and breathes in water and lays eggs as it swims. When the eggs hatch the young find their own food. It has 6 legs, a hard shell and scales. It has very small eyes and it is almost completely blind but has an acute sense of hearing. Animal B feeds all year round, often camouflaging itself while lying in wait for passing small fish. It also regularly eats seaweed. Animal B will mate with a different partner each year. It has large sharp teeth.

Animal C

This animal has wings, two legs and is covered in feathers. It hunts from the air, feeding only on small rodents and birds. It relies on its speed and excellent eyesight to catch its prey. It hasn't got any teeth but uses its sharp beak to tear apart its prey. It lays eggs in a nest, incubating them until they are hatched. Once hatched the offspring are fed meat by their parents until they are able to fly. The parents will remain together for life. Animal C has to hunt throughout the year.

Q1 Pick out four things that are different about the appearances (e.g. teeth) of the three animals.

Draw a table to summarise the differences.

Q2 Pick out four things that are different about the behaviour (e.g. feeding) of the three animals.

Draw a table to summarise the differences.

Sorting Things into Groups

Q1   Below are shown a number of fish. They have been sorted into two groups.

Group 1   **Group 2**

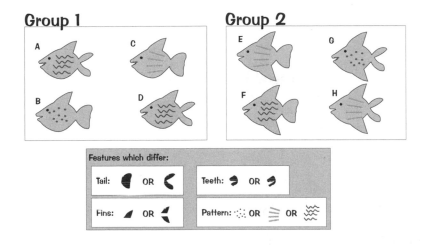

a)   What characteristic separates the fish into the groups above?

b)   How many characteristics differ among these fish?

c)   Put the fish into two groups according to their tail shape.

d)   Abdul puts C, E and H into a group.

    i)   What characteristic has Abdul used to create this group?

    ii)   How might you separate the remainder into further groups?

Q2   Four different insects are shown along with a key for identifying them.

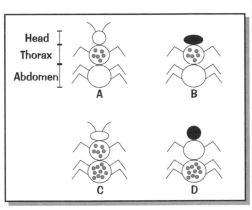

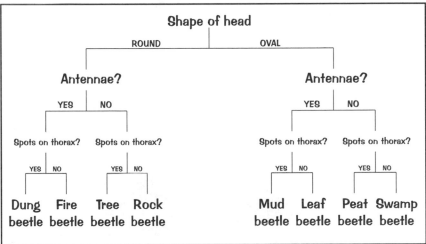

a)   Use the key to find the names of the insects.

b)   What other features could be used to identify the insects?

That's groupings explained then — sorted...

Biologists look for differences in animals in order to split them up into groups. They use these differences to make keys. Keys are just a list of questions which identify an animal (like in Q2).

How Scientists Classify Living Things

Q1 Copy and complete the diagram below showing how part of the
animal kingdom is classified by filling in the missing labels A, B, C and D.

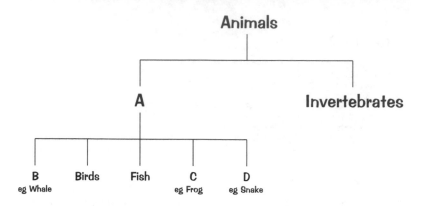

Animals

A | **Invertebrates**

B **Birds** **Fish** **C** **D**
eg Whale   eg Frog eg Snake

Q2 A scientist has found an animal and she wishes to classify it.

What's the first thing that the scientist must investigate
to decide which of the 2 main groups it belongs to?

Q3 Look at this selection of different animals.
Then use the diagram in Q1 to answer the questions below.

Bear   Snake   Ant   Lizard

Bee   Bird   Snail   Fish

Toad   Brontosaurus   Spider   Worm

a) List the vertebrates.

b) List the invertebrates.

c) Identify a mammal. What features make it a mammal?

d) Identify an amphibian. What features make it an amphibian?

e) Arthropods are invertebrates with jointed legs. List the arthropods shown above.

Some Acids and Alkalis

Q1   Copy and complete the passage using the words in the grey box.

ASPIRIN	DILUTING	LEMON JUICE	SOUR-TASTING	VINEGAR	WATER

Acids and alkalis can be found around the home. Acids can

be used in cooking: they are .... substances like

.... and .... If a dangerous acid or

alkali is spilled it can be made safer by .... it with

.... Some medicines like .... are weak acids.

Q2   List five acids from the household substances below.

Coca-Cola   Water   Tomato sauce   Shampoo

Orange juice   Bleach   Milk

Aspirin   Vitamin C tablets   Washing up liquid

Q3   Choose three from the six hazard symbols below that you
think you would find on a container of dangerous acid or alkali.

A
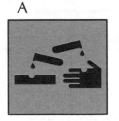

B
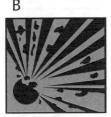

C
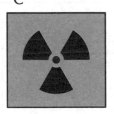

D

E

F
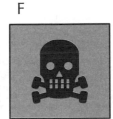

Q4   Below is a list of acids and alkalis found around the house.
Some are non-hazardous and some should have hazard warning labels.
Put them into two groups: hazardous and non-hazardous.

Lime juice	Mayonnaise	Battery acid
Drain cleaner	Vitamin-C	Baking soda
Vinegar	Toilet cleaner	Toothpaste
Bleach	Pickle	

Some Acids and Alkalis

Q1 **Sulfuric acid** is used to fill car batteries. It is a strong acid and can damage skin and clothing. Make a small poster about what safety measures you would take when filling a car battery with **sulfuric acid** and say what you would do in case of a spill.

Q2 You are the science reporter for the Haztown Daily News.
Rearrange the five sentences below to make a front page story about the tanker crash.

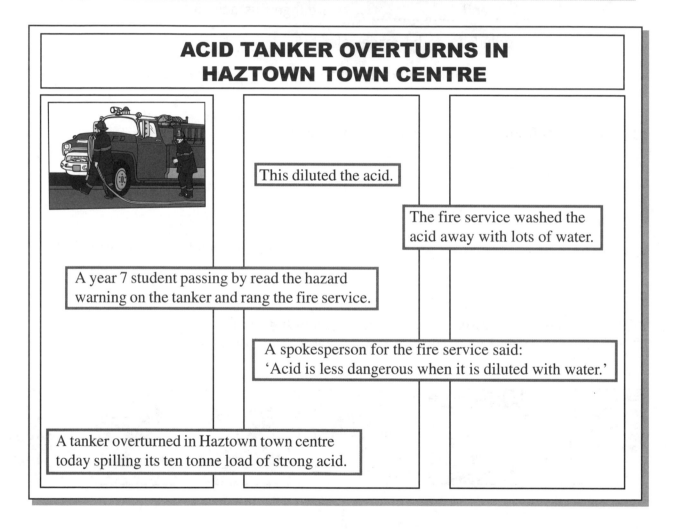

ACID TANKER OVERTURNS IN HAZTOWN TOWN CENTRE

This diluted the acid.

The fire service washed the acid away with lots of water.

A year 7 student passing by read the hazard warning on the tanker and rang the fire service.

A spokesperson for the fire service said:
'Acid is less dangerous when it is diluted with water.'

A tanker overturned in Haztown town centre today spilling its ten tonne load of strong acid.

Q3 Spray oven cleaner contains a strong alkali called **sodium hydroxide**. It can damage skin and is particularly dangerous to eyes and lungs.

Write a set of **instructions** explaining how to use the cleaner safely, including advice on what to do if some gets on your skin.

Acids and Alkalis — don't take sides, it's best to stay neutral...

As well as melting the Joker's face and making a great Batman film possible, acids have loads of more down to earth uses in batteries, cleaners and in lots of foods. And like Batman has Robin, acid has its faithful partner in crime, alkali. Hmm, how many superhero analogies can one tip hold?

Some Acids and Alkalis

Q1 Copy and complete the writing using the words from the grey box.

> BLACKCURRANT   COLOUR   INDICATORS   ACIDS

Some dyes change .... when you mix them with .... or alkalis.

We call these dyes .... Some examples of indicators are litmus,

.... juice and red cabbage solution.

Q2 Red cabbage indicator is **red** in acid and **turquoise** or **yellow** in alkali. Copy the table and fill in the empty column to show whether each substance is an **acid** or an **alkali**.

Substance	Colour in red cabbage indicator	Acid or alkali?
Lemon juice	Red	
Soapy bathwater	Turquoise	
Vinegar	Red	
Drain cleaner	Yellow	
Washing up liquid	Turquoise	
Lemonade	Red	

Q3 Copy the names of the substances. Next to each one, write down the colour you would see if you mixed it with litmus. Litmus indicator is **red** in acid and **blue** in alkali.

a) hydrochloric acid
b) nitric acid
c) sodium hydroxide (an alkali)
d) sulfuric acid
e) ammonium hydroxide (an alkali)

Q4 Write down the first letter of each answer to spell a word:

a) These make red cabbage indicator go red.
b) This indicator goes red in acid and blue in alkali.
c) A baby cat.
d) These make litmus go blue.
e) A yellow acidic fruit.
f) Litmus and blackcurrant juice are both ....

Q5 Use the information on this page to write down:

a) Two acids you can eat or drink.
b) Two foods you can use to make indicators.
c) Two alkalis you can use at home.
d) Two acids you can use in a science lesson.

The pH Scale

Q1 Copy and complete the passage by choosing the correct word from each highlighted pair.

Universal indicator is a mixture of dyes. It gives lots of different colours. A strong acid makes universal indicator go **[red / yellow]** and a strong alkali makes it go **[blue / green]**. In a neutral solution universal indicator is **[blue / green]**.

Q2 Copy and complete the diagram by choosing the correct words from the circle.

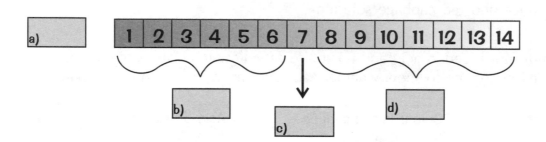

a)

| 1 | 2 | 3 | 4 | 5 | 6 | 7 | 8 | 9 | 10 | 11 | 12 | 13 | 14 |

b)

c)

d)

pH
ALKALIS
ACIDS
NEUTRAL

Q3 Choose one pH number from the list to go with each solution:
(pH numbers to choose from: pH1 pH5 pH7 pH9 pH14)

a) A neutral solution.
b) A strongly alkaline solution.
c) A weakly acidic solution.
d) A weakly alkaline solution.
e) A strongly acidic solution.

Q4 Use the table to write down the names of:

a) **two** weak acids

b) **two** neutral liquids

c) **three** alkaline solutions

d) **two** strong acids

Solution	pH
Washing up liquid	9
Lemon juice	3
Car battery acid (sulfuric acid)	1
Water	7
Sodium hydroxide	14
Rainwater	5
Oven cleaner	12
Blood	7
Stomach acid (hydrochloric acid)	2

Q5 Mary saw this symbol on a bottle of drain cleaner containing sodium hydroxide (pH14).

Write down **two** safety precautions she should take when she uses the drain cleaner.

Neutralising Acids and Alkalis

Q1   Copy and complete the passage by choosing the correct word from the grey box.

14   NEUTRAL   NEUTRALISED   ACIDIC   ACID   ALKALI   LOWER

Sodium hydroxide is an .... Its pH is .... If you add .... to sodium hydroxide the pH gets lower. When the pH is 7, the solution is .... — the acid has .... the alkali. If you add more acid the pH gets even .... The solution is now ....

Q2   Write down the **five** true statements from the list below:

a) Sam's hair shampoo is pH5.5. It is neutral.
b) Wasp stings are alkaline. You can treat them with lemon juice (pH3).
c) Acid rain can make lakes too acidic for some fish.
    You can add alkali to make a lake less acidic.
d) Nettle stings contain methanoic acid. You can neutralise them with vinegar (pH3).
e) Cola drinks are acidic and can damage tooth enamel.
f) Vinegar is acidic and is used to preserve food.
g) The hydrochloric acid in your stomach can kill some bacteria.

Q3   Use the table to decide whether to add an **alkali**, an **acid** or **nothing** to the soil.

Food Crop	pH at which the crop grows best
Potatoes	4-6
Peanuts	5-6
Grapes	6-7

a) The soil on Liz's field is pH8. She wants to grow potatoes. What should she add?
b) The soil on Nzila's farm is pH6. He wants to grow peanuts. What should he add?
c) The soil on Frank's farm is pH5. He wants to grow grapes. What should he add?

Q4   Clare does an experiment to see how the pH changes when she adds acid to an alkali. The hydrochloric acid and sodium hydroxide both have the same concentration.

Choose the correct results table and copy it out:

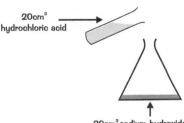

20cm³
hydrochloric acid

20cm³ sodium hydroxide solution and
a few drops of universal indicator
solution.

A

Volume of acid/cm³	Colour of indicator	pH
0	Blue	14
20	Red	7

B

Volume of acid/cm³	Colour of indicator	pH
0	Blue	14
20	Green	7

C

Volume of acid/cm³	Colour of indicator	pH
0	Blue	14
20	Green	1

The Importance of Neutralisation

Q1 Copy and complete the passage by choosing the correct word from the grey box.

> ALKALINE   ACID   HYDROCHLORIC   NEUTRALISE

You may get stomach ache if you have too much .... acid in your stomach.
Indigestion tablets dissolve in water to make .... solutions. These tablets
.... some of the .... in your stomach and make you feel better.

Q2 You have 3 different types of indigestion tablet. From the list
copy out **two** questions you could investigate to help you find
out which type of tablet is the best for curing indigestion.

    a) Which tablet tastes the best?
    b) How many tablets do you need to neutralise $50cm^3$ of hydrochloric acid?
    c) If you add one tablet to $50cm^3$ of hydrochloric acid, what is the final pH?
    d) How long does it take for a tablet to react with hydrochloric acid?

Q3 Amardeep is doing an experiment to find out the pH change when she puts an
indigestion tablet in $50cm^3$ of acid. Write out these instructions in the correct order.

    a) Measure out $50cm^3$ of hydrochloric acid in a measuring cylinder.
    b) Stir well.
    c) Crush up a tablet in a pestle and mortar and add it to the acid.
    d) Write down the pH of the acid.
    e) Pour the acid into a beaker.
    f) Look at the final colour of the indicator and write down the pH.
    g) Add 5 drops of universal indicator to the acid and look at its colour.

Q4 Junior is doing an experiment to find out what mass of tablet he needs to add
to hydrochloric acid to make it change from pH1 (acidic) to pH7 (neutral).
Write down **two** things he must do to make the experiment **fair**.

Q5 Grottwiggle has accidentally discovered a new
powder — Maginewt. A very small mass of
Maginewt neutralises a large volume of acid.
Write down **two** things Grottwiggle
must find out before she can sell
the powder as an indigestion cure.

Oh thanks Grottwiggle.
My stomach feels much better now.

It's supposed to turn
you into a newt!!!

Who's the best — Danni my pet newt or Uncle Al? Newt-or-Al...

And on that hilarious note, you'll be pleased to know this is the last page of the section.
So remember, you need acid in your stomach, but too much can give you quite a belly ache.
Indigestion tablets make an alkaline solution to neutralise some of the acid and make you feel better.

Chemical Reactions

Q1   Solve the following anagrams.

(Each one is something that you might detect if a chemical reaction has occurred)

a) erapmtueret sire   d) ooclur nhaceg

b) sublbeb fo sag   e) mealf

c) melsl

Q2   Chemical reactions make **new materials** — they're **irreversible changes.**
Make a table to show which of the following changes are **chemical reactions**,
and which are **physical changes**.

a)   Burning toast under a grill.

b)   Turning water into ice in the freezer.

c)   Boiling an egg.

d)   Igniting a Bunsen Burner.

e)   Salt disappearing as it's stirred into a beaker of water.

f)   Water droplets forming on a kitchen window near a kettle of boiling water.

g)   Green copper carbonate powder turning to black copper oxide when it's heated strongly.

Q3   Write down two differences between a **chemical reaction** and a **physical change**.

Q4   A teacher is showing his class that a gas is released
when bicarbonate of soda is added to lemon juice.

a)   How can you tell that a gas is released?

b)   Is this a physical change or a chemical change?

Chemical reactions — as easy as boiling an egg...
Remember — if it's an <u>irreversible</u> change, it's been caused by a <u>chemical reaction</u>.

Acids and Metals Reactions

Q1 Kirsty's teacher has made and collected some **hydrogen** gas as shown in the picture.

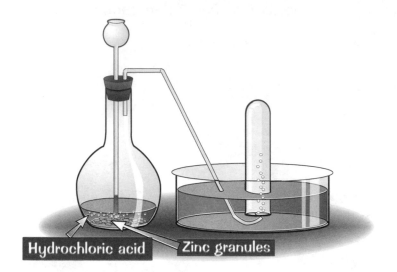

Hydrochloric acid   Zinc granules

It's just water — honest.

a) Write down **two** changes that Kirsty should **see** during the reaction.

b) Describe how Kirsty's teacher should test the gas collected to show that it is hydrogen.

Q2 Kirsty's teacher tried a second and a third experiment using two different metals.
In the second experiment, no gas was produced.
In the third experiment, gas was produced very quickly.

a) Which metal might Kirsty's teacher have used in:

i) the second experiment?

ii) the third experiment?

b) What gas was produced in the third experiment?

Q3 Copy the following paragraph, filling in the missing words. Choose words from the grey box.

When an acid is added to many metals such as .... the gas

produced is .... In this type of chemical ....

the piece of metal .... or becomes smaller.

You can describe acids as ....

reaction, graphite, zinc, air, hydrogen, corrosive, disappears, appears, burns

Acids and Carbonate Reactions

Q1   Which of the materials below contain mainly **carbonate** compounds?

soap   copper   limestone   wood

marble   baking powder   chalk

Q2   Lisa carried out a **chemical reaction** to show what gas is produced when an acid is added to limestone chips.

(Limestone is mostly calcium carbonate)

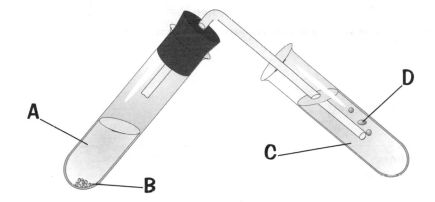

a)   Copy the diagram and name the things labelled A to D.

b)   What change can you see when carbon dioxide gas is bubbled through limewater?

Q3   Which of the following sentences are **true** and which are **false**?

a)   The 'fizz' in fizzy drinks is carbon dioxide gas.

b)   The gas produced when an acid is added to a carbonate is hydrogen.

c)   Limewater is used to test for carbon dioxide gas.

d)   Indigestion medicines often contain carbonates.

e)   The only acid that will react with a carbonate is hydrochloric acid.

f)   A chemical reaction always means new substances being made.

Making hydrogen — it's just a gas...

Don't get your gases mixed up. If you react <u>metals</u> with acid, it'll be <u>hydrogen</u>. If you react a <u>carbonate</u> with acid you'll get <u>carbon dioxide</u>. Remember — <u>carbon</u>ates make <u>carbon</u> dioxide.

Unit 7F — Simple Chemical Reactions

Burning Reactions

Q1 | Copy the paragraph, filling in the gaps using words from the white box.

Burning is a type of .... When a material burns,

it reacts with the .... in the .... to

produce a substance called an ....

Burning is an .... change.

> air irreversible oxygen
>
> oxide chemical reaction

Q2 | Copy and complete the word equations below.

Reactants			Products
magnesium	+	oxygen	→	....
iron	+	....	→	iron oxide
zinc	+	oxygen	→	....
....	+	oxygen	→	sulphur dioxide

Q3 | It's important for teachers and pupils to carry out combustion reactions **safely**.

A teacher is going to demonstrate to her class that burning a piece of magnesium ribbon in air is different from burning it in pure oxygen gas.

a) Write down four safety precautions that the teacher should take for herself and her class at all times during (and immediately after) her demonstration.

b) Write down **two** differences that the class should see between the two reactions.

Tie a magnesium ribbon round an old oak tree — then set fire to it...

Aahh... this is what Science is all about — burning things. Er... I mean heating things until they react with the oxygen in the air, glow red, emit flames and form oxides. Or something.

Burning Reactions

Q1   David's teacher demonstrated a useful reaction involving burning a fuel.

to pump

limewater (tests for CO_2)

Cold ice/water mixture

a) i) What product of the reaction was the teacher collecting in the U-tube?

   ii) Why did David's teacher need to cool the U-tube?

b) i) What **product** of the reaction was being bubbled through the limewater?

   ii) What **change** would David see in the limewater when the fuel was being burned?

Q2   The statements below are **wrong**.
      Write them out again, replacing the word in **bold** type with a more suitable word.

a) Ethanol, **glass** and wax are examples of fuels.

b) Fossil fuels are rich in a substance called **tin.**

c) **Mixing** fossil fuels releases energy.

d) Natural gas is called **wax.**

e) Carbon dioxide and **nitrogen** are produced when a fuel burns.

Q3   Copy and complete the word equation which shows what happens
      when a fuel called **methane** (natural gas) is burned.

   methane + o............ → .... + ... + energy

You Tarzan — Me Thane...
Remember — when you burn things, <u>energy</u> is produced. If there's <u>a lot</u> of energy, chemists often <u>write it in the equation</u> as one of the products of the reaction. But don't let that confuse you — energy's <u>not</u> a <u>substance</u>, you <u>can't see it</u> or <u>touch it</u> and it <u>doesn't</u> have <u>mass</u>. It's weird stuff.

Burning Reactions

Q1   A group of year 7 pupils set up the experiment shown in the diagram.

They placed a large glass container quickly over the
burning candle and timed how long the candle stayed alight.

a)   After 29 seconds the candle went out. Why?

b)   Why didn't the candle go out as soon as the glass container was put over it?

c)   What happened to the level of water in the glass container?

d)   Explain your answer to c).

e)   Which part of the air was used up in the glass container?

Q2   Another group of pupils in the class burned a candle in a series of different-sized beakers,
upside down. They timed how long the candle stayed alight in each one.

Here is a graph of their results:

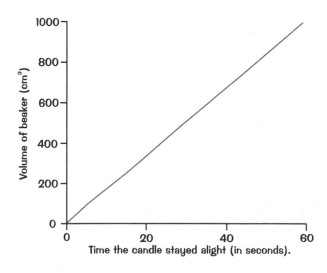

a)   What **relationship** does the graph show between the size
of the beaker and the time the candle stayed alight?

b)   Explain **why** this relationship occurs.

c)   Estimate how long their candle would have stayed alight in a beaker of volume **2000cm³**.

Explaining Evidence from Experiments

Q1 Copy the names of the substances. Next to each one, write down whether it is a solid, liquid or gas at room temperature:

a) gold   e) paper   h) petrol

b) water   f) vinegar   i) carbon dioxide

c) oxygen   g) diamond   j) salt

d) wood

Liquids are useless for some things.

Q2 Both these blocks are the same size.
Copy out the 2 sentences which explain why the block of gold has a greater mass than the block of aluminium.

A gold particle has a greater mass than an aluminium particle.

A particle of gold is lighter than a particle of aluminium.

The gold particles are further apart than the aluminium particles.

The gold particles are closer together than the aluminium particles.

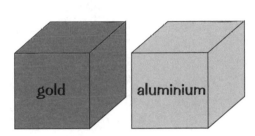

Q3 The ends of these syringes are sealed so that nothing can come out of them. Copy the paragraph below, choosing the correct word from each highlighted pair.

You [can't / can] push in the plungers in the sand and water syringes. This is because the particles in the sand and water are very [far apart / close together].

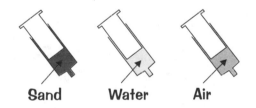

The particles in the air syringe are [far apart / close together] to start with.
When you push in the plunger, the air particles get [further apart / closer together].

Q4 This picture shows the particles in a bottle of perfume.

a) Draw a diagram to show what happens to the perfume vapour particles when you take the lid off the bottle.

b) Explain why someone close to the bottle smells the perfume before someone who is further away.

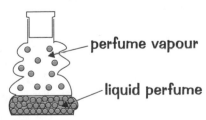

Science is just like perfume — gets right up your nose...

It doesn't matter how many times they tell you this stuff, it's still dead weird. A solid's just a load of little particles. So how does it stay together — "forces of attraction", they say. Hmmm...

Explaining Evidence from Experiments

Q1 At room temperature, the metal rod fits through the hole (just!). If you heat the rod to a high temperature, it doesn't fit through the hole.

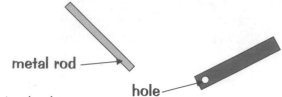

metal rod

hole

Copy the writing and fill in the gaps using the words in the box.

faster	further	big	slowly	particles

When the metal rod is cold, its particles vibrate .... on the spot.

When the bar is hotter, the particles vibrate .... The vibrating

.... hit each other, and get .... apart. This makes the

end of the rod too .... to fit through the hole.

Q2 Marcus stuck paper clips onto one end of a copper rod using candle wax. He heated the other end of the rod. Gradually the heat travelled down the rod, the wax melted and the paper clips fell off.

copper rod

heat
(bunsen flame)

paper clips held on with wax

Copy sentences A, B, C and pictures 1, 2, 3. Match each sentence to the correct picture.

(A) The particles vibrate very fast when heated.

(B) They hit the particles next to them and make them vibrate faster. This part of the rod is now hot.

(C) These particles hit other particles further down the rod and make them vibrate faster too.

(1)

(2)

(3)

Q3 Samira hung 10g weights on a metal wire. It snapped when she had added 200g. Write 3 sentences to explain why the wire snapped.

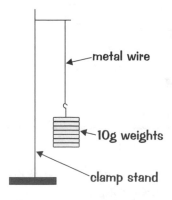

metal wire

10g weights

clamp stand

For each sentence, use one phrase from each of the three columns:

10g	The particles in the middle of the wire are so far apart that the wire snaps	and the forces between the particles are slightly less strong.
200g	The particles are very close together	and the forces between these particles are now too weak to hold them together.
160g	The particles are very far apart	and the forces between the particles are very strong.

How Theories are Created

Q1   Copy this writing and fill in the gaps using words from the cloud.

theories   explain   experiments   observations   evidence   change

Scientists collect ...., usually by doing experiments or

making .... Then they think of ideas to .... the

evidence. These ideas are called .... Later, scientists may do more ....

and get some new evidence. Then they might have to .... their first theory.

Q2   Read the writing then answer these questions:

a) Who entered the shop first? Write down **four** pieces of evidence that support your theory.

b) Write down **two** pieces of evidence that you ignored when you made your theory.

> A mobile phone shop has been burgled. Police officers found 3 brothers inside the shop. A witness said that she saw a man climb a ladder and squeeze through a very small skylight in the roof before letting the other 2 brothers in through the door. You have the following evidence:
>
> - Aidan has a broken leg that was in plaster.
>
> - Aidan can't swim.
>
> - Jason is very fat.
>
> - Jason is afraid of heights.
>
> - Jason was eating a pasty when the police arrived.
>
> - Matthew goes to the gym often.

Q3   Here is a list of four theories. Copy the list. Next to each theory write down the letter (W, X, Y or Z) for the piece of evidence that supports the theory.

The Theories:
a) Particles in liquids are closer together than particles in gases.
b) Gas particles spread out to fill as much space as possible.
c) Particles in solids get slightly further apart when you heat them.
d) Particles of different substances have different masses.

The Evidence:

W The smell from someone wearing too much (or too little) deodorant spreads all round the room.	**X** Metal rods expand when they get hot.
Y A gold ring has a greater mass than an aluminium ring of the same size.	**Z** You <u>can</u> push in the plunger of a sealed syringe with air in it. You <u>can't</u> push in the plunger of a sealed syringe of water.

Theories — they're just ideas with bells on...

You see — I have a theory, right. I reckon that the world's actually flat. And that people who *claim* they've "sailed round the world" should be burnt at the stake, frankly. That's what I reckon.

Solids, Liquids and Gases

Q1   Solids, liquids and gases behave in different ways because they have different properties.
Copy this table and use the phrases below to fill in the empty boxes.

Property	Solids	Liquids	Gases
Volume	Definite volume		
Shape		Match shape of container	
Density			Very low density
Ease of Flow	Don't flow		

Phrases to use: *definite shape, definite volume, flow easily, medium density, flow easily, high density, match shape of container, no definite volume — fill their container*

Q2   The key below can be used to decide if something is a solid, a liquid or a gas. Copy the key and fill in the gaps.

a)   Does it have a fixed volume?

   YES   — Go to b).

   NO   — Go to ....

b)   Does it have a definite shape?

   YES   — Go to c).

   NO   — Go to d).

c)   It is a ....

d)   It is a ....

e)   It is a gas.

*Alternative method:
consult giant horned lizard.*

Q3   Copy the names of the substances. Next to each one write down whether it is a solid, liquid or gas and give a reason for your answer.

a) sand

b) chewing gum

c) tomato sauce

d) toothpaste

e) hairspray

The Particle Model

Q1 Copy the names of the substances. Next to each one, write down whether it's a solid, liquid or gas:

a) ice b) drinking water c) steam

Q2 Solids, liquids and gases are made of tiny particles. Fill in the boxes to show the arrangement of particles in ice, liquid water and steam:

ice liquid water steam

Q3 Copy this table. Use the phrases below to fill in the empty boxes.

	Solids	Liquids	Gases
How close are the particles?			
How do the particles move?			

Phrases to use: *vibrate on the spot, move past each other in all directions, very close, far apart, move fast in all directions, very close*

Q4 Write out the **six** true sentences from the list below:

— *Strong forces hold the particles together in solids.*
— *Particles in liquids vibrate on the spot.*
— *Solid particles are arranged in a regular pattern.*
— *Weak forces hold the particles together in solids.*
— *Quite strong forces hold the particles together in liquids.*

— *It is difficult to compress liquids.*
— *It is difficult to compress gases.*
— *Gases expand to fill their container.*
— *Gas particles move slowly.*
— *Gas particles collide often with each other.*

Q5 Barney drew this picture to show how the particles are arranged in a glass of water. List **three** mistakes he has made.

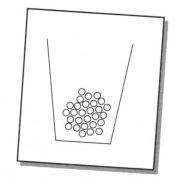

Fixed volume — mine's stuck on loud...
If you get all these right, you've got a pretty good understanding of solids, liquids and gases.

Using the Particle Model

Q1 Sasha lets off a stink bomb. After a few minutes Chesney can smell it at the other end of the corridor. Copy the writing and fill in the gaps to explain why.

Words to use: *spread, particles, lots, few, diffusion*

To start with, there are .... of smell particles where the stink bomb is. Gradually,

they .... out. The smell .... have moved from where there are lots of them

to where there are only a .... of them. This process is called ....

Q2 At the cinema, you can often see dust particles in the beam of light. Write down **three** sentences from the list below to explain why the dust particles are moving around.

— *The light gives the dust particles energy to move.* — *Air particles move around all the time.*
— *Air particles bump into dust particles.* — *Dust particles vibrate in time with the pictures.*
— *Cinemas attract especially energetic dust.*
— *When an air particle bumps into a dust particle, the dust particle moves off in a different direction.*

Q3 Edward put a grey crystal on some agar gel. After a few days, the grey colour had spread out a bit. Copy the diagram and add some grey particles to show how the colour spread.

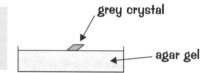

Q4 Esmerelda puts one big green sweet in a glass of cold water and another big green sweet in a glass of hot water. Copy the writing below, choosing one word from each highlighted pair.

In both glasses, [water / air] particles bump into

the sweet. Some green particles come off the

sweet and mix in with the water particles.

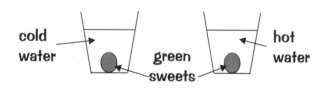

Esmerelda can see green solutions in both glasses. Hot water particles move

[slower / faster] than cold water particles, so particles come off the sweet more

often in [hot / cold] water. After 20 minutes, more particles will have come off the

sweet in the hot water, so the hot solution will be [lighter / darker] green.

Q5 This glass has a layer of black ink underneath the water. After a few hours the water becomes black too. Write a few sentences to explain why the black colour spreads out — mention particles in your answer.

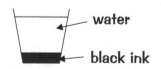

Diffusion — learn it now before it all drifts away...

It's like if you have a dancefloor full of people all jumping around and then they open another bit of dancefloor — people gradually spread out onto both dancefloors. High to low concentration, see.

Unit 7G — Solids, Liquids and Gases

Mixtures

Q1   Seawater is mainly a mixture of water, dissolved salts and sand.
      Distilled water is much more like pure water.

   a) What does the word 'pure' mean in science?

   b) What does the word 'mixture' mean in science?

   c) Write down three examples of a mixture you might find at home.

   d) Which of the liquids below are mixtures?

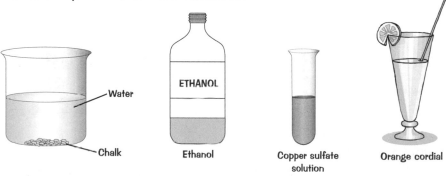

Water — Chalk   ETHANOL   Copper sulfate   Orange cordial
                       Ethanol   solution

Q2   Some solids dissolve in liquids to make a solution and some don't.

   a) What word is used in science to mean that something does dissolve?

   b) What word is used in science to mean that something does not dissolve?

   c) Name two everyday substances that will dissolve in water.

   d) Name two everyday substances that will not dissolve in water.

Q3   When solid copper sulfate dissolves in water it turns the water a blue colour.

   a) How do you know that the copper sulfate has dissolved and not disappeared?

   b) How could you separate the copper sulfate from
      the water to show that it has not disappeared?

Q4   Unscramble the words below to reveal four key words to do with dissolving.

   a) bloules   c) outsel

   b) losbunile   d) tulsooni

Q5   How could you separate chalk from water using simple lab apparatus?

Q6   If you had a clear liquid in a beaker, how could you
      tell if it was a mixture or whether it was pure?

Rock Salt

You're given a 10 g sample of rock salt which contains a mixture of rock and salt.
You carry out an investigation to find out how much of the rock salt was actually pure salt.

Q1   The Aim:

What is the aim of the investigation? (i.e. what are you trying to find out?)

Q2   The Apparatus:

List the apparatus you would use.
Then draw out a labelled diagram to show how the apparatus would be set up and used.

Q3   The Method:

a) How would you check that you really have a 10 g sample of rock salt to start with?

b) What can you do with the rock salt to dissolve the salt?

c) How can you then separate the rock from the salty water?

d) How can you separate the salt from the salty water?

e) How can you find out how much salt you have at the end of the investigation?

Q4   The Results:

When the pure salt was weighed the scales read 3000 mg. How many grams is this?

Q5   The Conclusion:

a) As a percentage (%) of the original mass how much of the rock salt was salt?
   (Clue: 2 g of salt out of 10 g of rock salt would mean 20% of it was salt.)

b) How might you improve the investigation to make it more accurate?

Finding out about salt? Do an experiment — that's the solution...

These questions cover loads about separating rock salt. They're also a top reminder of how to do
and write up experiments — Aim, Apparatus, Method, Results, Conclusion. Simple.

Solutes and Solutions

Q1   Read Jack's experiment and then answer the questions.

Jack weighed out 15.00 g of table salt using a
digital balance. He then carefully poured out
100 cm³ of water using a measuring cylinder.

He found that the water had a mass of 100 g.
He mixed the salt and the water in a beaker
then stirred the mixture to dissolve the salt and
make a solution. Finally he weighed the solution.

a) Why did Jack use a digital balance?

b) What was the mass (in grams) of the mixture of salt and water?

c) Explain your answer to b).

d) Jack tried to separate the salt and the water by filtering the solution.
   Explain why filtering could not separate the salt from the water.

Q2   Jack weighed a large evaporating basin (mass 46.32 g) and transferred the solution to
it from the beaker. He left the evaporating dish in a hot sunny place near a window
over the holidays. When he returned there were white crystals in the dish.

a) What were the white crystals left in the dish?

b) Where had the water gone?

c) What name do we give to this way of separating substances?

d) Jack reweighed the dish with the crystals, and found that it had a mass of 61.32g.
   What mass of crystals where in the dish?

e) What does this show about dissolving substances?

Q3   When things mix, their particles intermingle. The diagram
shows particles of salt and water before they are mixed.

Complete the picture of the third beaker to show what you think the particles
will look like if they are mixed. Clearly label the particles of salt and water.

Separating Solvents and Solutes

Q1 Blue ink is a mixture of coloured dyes and water. It can be separated into the dyes and water using this apparatus.

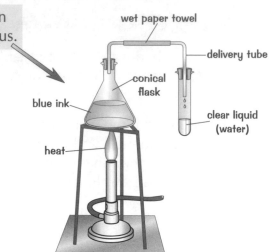

a) Why is the ink heated?

b) What do the wet paper towel and the delivery tube do?

c) Why is the water clear and not blue?

d) How could you check that the liquid was really pure water?

Q2 Distillation can be described using the following sentences. Write them down in the correct order to help explain the process of distillation.

a) The gas turns back to a liquid.

b) The liquid turns into a gas.

c) The pure liquid is collected.

d) The condenser cools the gas.

e) The gas travels to the cool condenser.

f) The liquid begins to boil.

g) The liquid and the solute are heated up.

Q3 Doris has unfortunately found herself ship-wrecked on a desert island and can't find any water. She thought back to her science lessons and remembered that she had learnt that pure water can be obtained from seawater. She found a sheet of old clear plastic and a tin can, which had washed up on the beach, and set up the following.

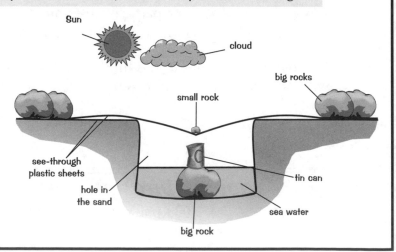

a) Explain in as much detail as possible how the water in the seawater finds its way into the can.

b) Why does the water not taste of salt, like seawater?

c) Most water is collected when the sun is shining brightly. Why is this?

Chromatography

Q1   From the following, only copy out the correct statements about chromatography.

   a) Chromatography is a separation technique.

   b) Chromatography can be used to separate coloured inks only.

   c) Chromatography involves boiling and condensing.

   d) Chromatography can be used to separate a mixture of solutes
      which are soluble in the same solvent.

   e) Chromatography is used to identify unknown substances.

Q2   Copy the diagram and fill in the names for labels a) to d).

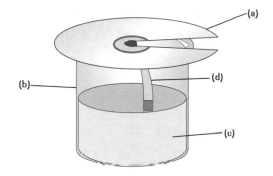

Q3   Explain how chromatography can be used to compare two substances that
      are found in the colouring of sugar-coated chocolate sweets, like Smarties.

Q4   Chromatography is used in forensic science.

   a) What is forensic science?

   b) Name an example where chromatography is used in forensic science.

Q5   To explain how chromatography works and the fact that certain substances travel
      different distances through the chromatogram, we can think of the solvent particles
      giving the solute particles a 'piggyback ride'. Using this idea and diagrams if you
      want, explain in detail how chromatography works.

Bob only photoed birds on rugs — he was a crow-mat-ographer...
Chromatography is definately one of the more interesting separation techniques.
After all, you can make loads of pretty patterns and pass it off as science.

Solubility

Q1 From the following, copy out only the correct statements about solubility.

a) When a soluble solid is added to an appropriate solvent, a solution is made.

b) When an insoluble solid is added to a solvent, a solution is made.

c) When a soluble solid is added to a solvent, there is a limit to how much can be dissolved.

d) When a soluble solid is added to a solvent, there isn't a limit to how much can be dissolved.

e) When a soluble solid is added to a solvent, the amount which dissolves depends on the temperature of the liquid.

f) When a soluble solid is added to a solvent, the amount which dissolves does not depend on the temperature of the liquid.

Q2 Sodium hydrogen carbonate (bicarbonate of soda) is soluble in water. Describe an experiment you could do in the lab, which would find out how much of it could be dissolved in 20 cm^3 of water.

Q3 The solubility of potassium nitrate fertiliser is 21 g per 100 g of water at 10 °C.

a) What does the above statement mean?

b) How many grams of potassium nitrate could be dissolved in 50 g of water?

c) How many grams of potassium nitrate could be dissolved in 200 g of water?

d) Why is it useful to know how soluble a fertiliser is?

e) Do you think that insoluble fertilisers would be useful or not? Explain your answer.

Q4 Choose the correct description of a saturated solution and write it out.

A saturated solution is...

a) ...a very wet solution.

b) ...a solution with a solute lying on the container bottom.

c) ...a damp answer to a dry question.

d) ...a solution where no more solute can be added.

More about Solubility

Q1 Look at the table below and answer the questions.

Table Showing Solubility at Room Temperature / g per 100g Water

Substance	Temperature / °C				
	20	30	40	50	60
A	25	30	37	46	59
B	32	33	35	38	42
C	29	31	33	35	37

a) Which is the most soluble substance at 20 °C?

b) Which is the least soluble substance at 20 °C?

c) How does the solubility of A, B and C change as the temperature is increased?

d) Why should you always quote the temperature when giving the solubility of a substance?

e) Which substance's solubility changes the most, as the temperature is increased?

Q2 The graph below shows how the solubility of sodium chloride (common salt) changes with temperature. Look at the graph and then answer the questions below it.

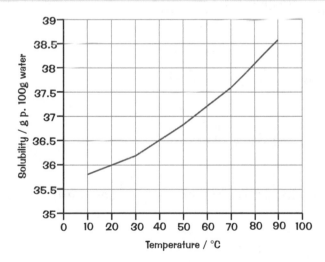

a) Describe how the solubility of sodium chloride changes as the temperature rises.

b) Using the graph, find what mass of sodium chloride can dissolve in 100 g of water at 30 °C.

c) What is the solubility of sodium chloride at 50 °C?

d) Estimate the solubility of sodium chloride at 100 °C.

e) If you had 10 g of water at 30 °C, how much salt would you add to get a saturated solution?

f) If 100 cm³ of solution was cooled from 60 °C to 40 °C, what mass of salt would
   come out of the solution? (i.e. stop being dissolved and appear as salt crystals.)

Uses of Fuels

Q1   Write down the type of fuel that would be used in each of the following:

a) a central heating system,

b) a camping stove,

c) a train,

d) a barbecue.

Q2   The pictures below show 4 uses of fuels.
Copy and complete the sentences for each one.

    a)   b)   c)   d)

a)   Petrol is b............. to make the car m..............

b)   Candle wax is b........... to give off l...........

c)   Coal is b........... to give off h...........

d)   Kerosene is b........... to make the plane m...........

Q3   **Movement**, **heat** and **light** are all types of what?

Q4   Copy and complete the equation below which summarises the burning of fuel:

FUEL + O................... → E...................

Q5   Copy the **correct** statements from this list about **good fuels**:

a) give out a lot of heat   f) are very flammable

b) give off a lot of smoke   g) burn with a smokey yellow flame

c) are easy to light   h) are very expensive

d) burn steadily   i) burn with a clean flame

e) give off toxic fumes   j) are easy to transport

Uses of Fuels

Q1 Write down 3 fossil fuels from the list below:

a) wood

e) seal blubber (a layer of fat under the skins of seals)

b) camel dung

f) a battery

c) natural gas

g) oil

d) coal

Q2 Coal is made from dead plants. What are oil and natural gas mostly made from?

Q3 Where are oil and natural gas formed?

Q4 Write out the following statements in the correct order, to describe how a fossil fuel is made:

a) Coal is made from plants that lived millions of years ago.

b) Water from swamps flowed over them and covered them with sand and mud.

c) As time passed the sand and mud changed to rock.

d) When the plants died they fell to the ground.

e) The plants couldn't rot because there was no oxygen around them.

f) The dead plants were squashed into a flat layer of coal.

New from *Sloda*

Low fuel consumption range:

Q5 Why are fossil fuels described as **non-renewable**? Use the key words below in your answer.

MILLIONS   YEARS   REPLACED   FAST   USE

Q6 Scientists predict that oil and natural gas supplies will run out by 2050.

a) How old will you be in 2050?

b) Give 2 ways in which life will be different if there is no oil or gas.

c) What would happen to the supplies of coal if the oil and gas ran out?

d) What could we do to make our energy supplies last longer? Give 2 suggestions.

If you're stuck, just burn your homework — it's a novel excuse...

The problem is, they all thought these fuels would be around for ever. D'oh.

Renewable Energy Resources

Q1   Using **some** of the words below, copy and complete the sentence.

CAN	FAST	RENEWABLE	CANNOT	SLOW

A .... energy resource is one that ....

be replaced as .... as it is being used.

Q2   The pictures below show devices which use renewable energy resources.
Name each device and the type of renewable energy that it uses.

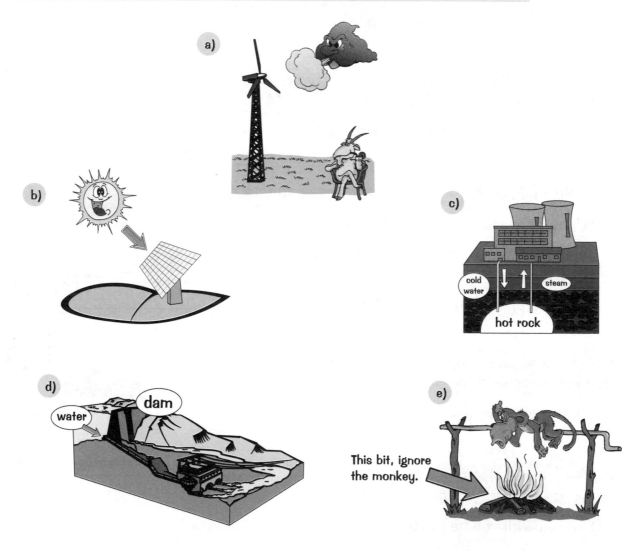

a)

b)

c)

cold water   steam

hot rock

d)

water   dam

e)

This bit, ignore the monkey.

Q3   Name one important renewable energy resource which has not been included in Q2.

No animals were harmed in the making of this page...

This is important stuff. If we can't think of alternative ways to harness energy, we'll all end up
sitting in the cold and dark through the long winter nights, without even a Playstation for company.

Renewable Energy Resources

Q1 You can summarise how the devices in Q2 on p.54 work by drawing a flow diagram e.g.

SOLAR PANEL

sunlight $\Rightarrow$ heats water in solar panel $\Rightarrow$ water is turned into steam $\Rightarrow$ steam turns a turbine $\Rightarrow$ turbine turns a generator $\Rightarrow$ generator makes electricity

Copy and complete these summaries for the other devices.

a) **WIND TURBINES**

.... turns the blades $\Rightarrow$ the blades turn a turbine $\Rightarrow$ the turbine turns a generator $\Rightarrow$ the generator makes ....

b) **HYDROELECTRIC POWER STATION**

falling w.............. $\Rightarrow$ the water turns a turbine $\Rightarrow$ the t............. turns a generator $\Rightarrow$ the .... makes ....

c) **GEOTHERMAL POWER STATION**

c........ water is pumped down into h....... rocks $\Rightarrow$ the water turns into s........ $\Rightarrow$ steams turns a turbine $\Rightarrow$ the turbine turns a .... $\Rightarrow$ generator makes electricity

d) What do the devices a) - c) all make?

Q2 Copy and complete the table to give one advantage and one disadvantage of each renewable energy resource.

Energy Resource	Advantage	Disadvantage
Solar		
Wind		
Geothermal		
Hydroelectric		
Biomass		

Spend some of your energy answering these...

Now what _would_ be handy would be if we could harness the energy of _drizzle_. Then at least _something_ good would come out of the fact that it chucks it down every single summer...

How Living Things Use Energy

Q1 For each living thing below, give an activity that it needs energy for.

a) a bird   **b) Joe**   **c) a tiger**   **d) a fish**

   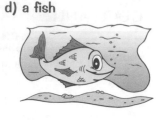

Q2 Copy and complete these sentences:

All living things need e _____ to carry out activities. They get energy from the f _____ they eat. Food is their energy r _____. Different foods contain different amounts of e _____. The energy in food is measured in j _____.

Q3 A joule is a very small amount of energy. How many joules are there in a kilojoule?

Q4 The table shows the amount of energy contained in different foods.

Food	Amount of energy kJ	Food	Amount of energy kJ	Food	Amount of energy kJ	Food	Amount of energy kJ
Cottage cheese	110	Vegetable Soup	400	Carrot	108	Grilled Chicken	840
Cheshire Cheese	890	Cream of tomato soup	565	Cabbage	80	Potatoes boiled	323
Lemonade	750	1 Slice of Bread	397	Baked beans	1450	Lettuce	20
Milk Full Cream	675	1 Banana	275	Jelly	425	Tuna fish	310
Milk Skimmed	370	1 Apple	190	Cherry cake	646	Chips	1150
Tea with Milk	200	Ice Cream	520	Fish finger	220	1 Plain Biscuit	162

a) Write down the food that contains the most energy.

b) Write the food that contains the least energy.

c) How much energy is in a banana sandwich made of 2 slices of bread, and a banana?

Q5 On average, a farmer needs 14,000kJ of energy per day and an office worker needs 10,000kJ of energy per day.

a) Explain why there is such a difference in the energy they need.

b) What might happen to the farmer if his daily intake of energy were only 10,000kJ?

c) What might happen to the office worker if his daily intake were 15,000kJ of energy?

Q6 After eating breakfast and lunch the office worker had taken in 6,000kJ of energy. Design an evening meal which would make sure that he takes in all the energy he needs for that day.

The Parts of an Electrical Circuit

Q1   Fill in the missing names and draw the missing circuit symbols.

SYMBOL	NAME
————	....
....	SWITCH
⊗ OR ⌒	....
Ⓥ	....
....	AMMETER
|ı|ı|ı	.... made of three ....

Q2   Using circuit symbols, draw the following circuits:

a)   A series circuit containing
      two cells, two bulbs and one switch.

b)   A parallel circuit containing two cells,
      two bulbs and two switches
      — **each switch should control one bulb only.**

Q3   Copy and complete the following statements
         by selecting the correct word from the grey box.

CAN	NEGATIVE	POSITIVE	ENERGY
CAN'T	COMPLETE	OPEN	CLOSED

a)   For a current to flow there must be a .... circuit.

b)   For a current to flow switches must be ....

c)   If there is a gap in a circuit the current .... flow.

d)   For a circuit to work two cells must be connected positive to ....

e)   A battery or power pack is a source of electrical ....

How Electrical Circuits Work

Q1 List the letters of the bulbs that will light in the following circuits.
Then **correct** each circuit so that **all** bulbs will light

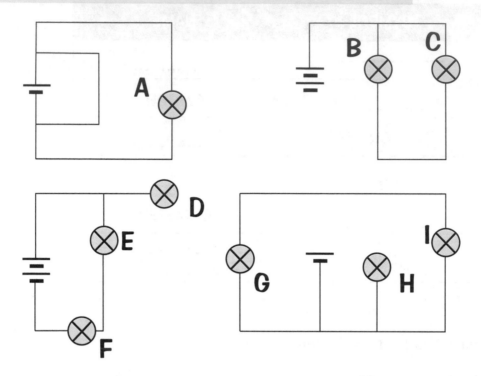

Q2 Study the following circuit:

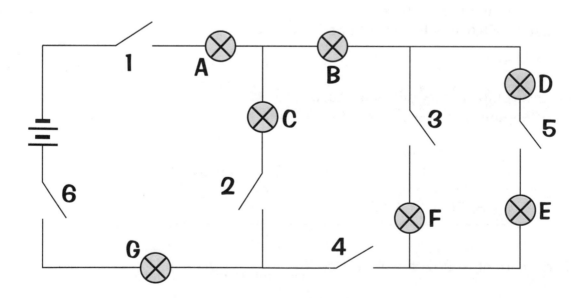

For each bulb (A-G) write down the switches that **MUST** be closed for the bulb to be lit.

LET THERE BE LIGHT — and there was *(once he'd found the switch)...*

If you can trace with your finger from one side of the battery <u>through</u> a bulb and back to the
<u>other side</u> of the battery <u>without any breaks</u> then the bulb will light. Try it.

What Happens in Circuits

Q1 The circuit symbol for an ammeter is shown below.

Copy the following sentences choosing the correct word from the options given.

An ammeter measures [**voltage** / **current** / **energy**].

Current is measured in [**joules** / **volts** / **amps**].

An ammeter must be connected in [**series** / **parallel**]

Q2 Two identical bulbs were connected in the following circuit.
The reading on ammeter X was 4A.

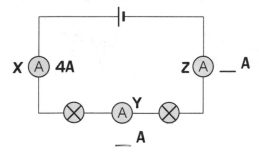

Copy the circuit and write down the readings on ammeters Y and Z.

Q3 Study the three circuits below.

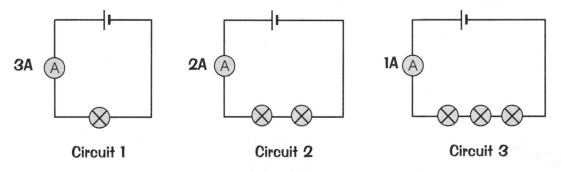

For each of the following statements say whether it is true or false.
If false then rewrite the sentence correctly.

a) As more bulbs are added the current increases.

b) As more bulbs are added the bulbs get dimmer.

c) Putting more bulbs in the circuit decreases the total resistance.

d) The bulbs in circuit 3 could be made brighter by adding another cell.

What Happens in Circuits

Q1   Cells provide voltage. Cells added together make a battery.
     Each of the cells below has a voltage of 1.5V.

A   **B**   **C**   **D**

For each battery write down the total voltage.

Q2   Study the circuits below. All bulbs and cells are identical.

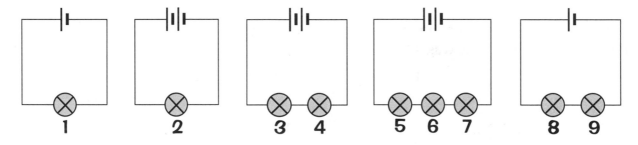

1   **2**   **3   4**   **5   6   7**   **8   9**

a)   Which bulb(s) is/are the brightest?

b)   Which bulb(s) is/are the dimmest?

c)   Which two bulbs have the same brightness as bulb 3?

Q3   The resistance of a variable resistor can be changed.

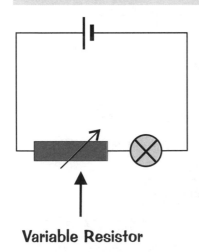

Variable Resistor

Initially the resistance of the variable resistor is low.

The bulb is bright.

a)   Is the current through the bulb high or low?

b)   The resistance of the variable resistor is
     increased. Explain what happens to the bulb.

You will learn this — resistance is futile...

The larger the voltage the larger the current. The lower the resistance the larger the current.
The larger the voltage the larger the current. The lower the resistance the larger the current. Got it?

Explaining Circuits

Q1 No current is lost at a junction. In the circuit below all the bulbs are identical.
Ammeter K reads 6A and ammeter L reads 2A.

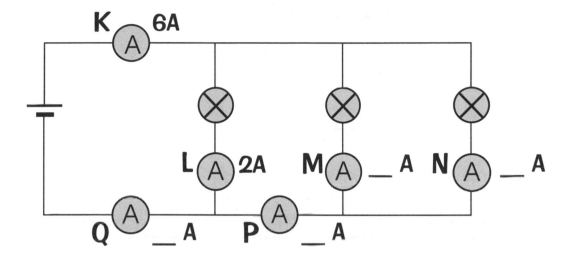

Copy the circuit and write down the readings on ammeters M, N, P and Q.

Q2 Asif suggests that a water circuit is like an electrical circuit.

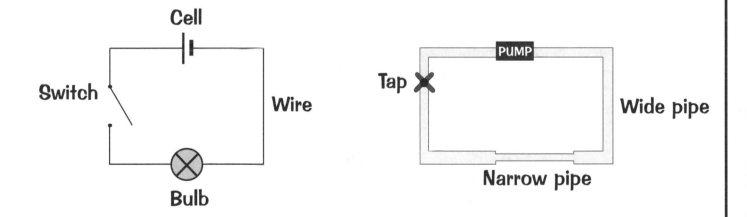

Asif says:

"The **_pump_** pushes the **_water_** around the circuit. It is easy to push the **_water_** through the **_wide pipes_**. The **_narrow pipe_** offers more resistance. Turning the **_tap_** off stops the flow of **_water_** throughout the whole circuit. To push more **_water_** you could use a higher **_power pump_**. To have less **_water_** flowing in the circuit put another **_narrow pipe_** in series."

If the **underlined** words are changed Asif could be describing the electrical circuit.
Rewrite the paragraph so that it describes the electrical circuit.

Explaining Circuits

Q1 Jane suggests a way to increase the water flowing through the pipes.
She adds another section of narrow pipe as shown below.

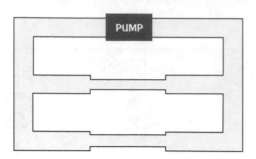

a) Copy and complete the following paragraph choosing the words from the grey box.

| SERIES | RESISTANCE | PARALLEL | WATER | MORE | LESS |

Jane has added another narrow pipe in .... with the first. There are now

.... pathways for the water to flow. There is less .... in the circuit.

The pump can push more .... around the circuit.

b) Now draw the electrical circuit that follows Jane's idea.

Q2 In the circuit below all bulbs are identical.
The ammeter E reads 12A and ammeter F reads 4A.

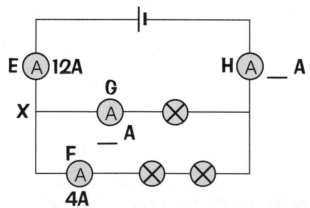

a) Copy the circuit and add the readings on ammeters G and H.

b) When the current reaches the junction at X it splits.
Why does more current go through the top branch than the bottom branch?
(Hint – use the word resistance in your answer)

Water circuits and electric circuits — not to be mixed...

All the current that leaves a battery will return. All the current that enters a junction leaves it.
No matter how hard you try, no current is lost — it's like your annoying little brother.

Useful Circuits and Their Hazards

Q1   Copy and complete the paragraph choosing the correct highlighted words.

The mains electricity in your home is supplied at a voltage of [115 / 230 / 1.5]V.
The voltage supplied by a torch battery is much [lower / higher]. Touching any
mains wires is extremely [safe / dangerous / clever], especially if you have [dry / wet] skin.
Wet skin has a lower [energy/voltage/resistance] than dry skin. This means that a
[large / small] current can flow through you — a current that is likely to
[amuse / kill / tickle] you.

Q2   There should be no 230V sockets in a bathroom. Explain why.

Q3   You might find a socket like the
one on the right in your bathroom.

Explain why it is safe.

Q4   A fuse melts and breaks the circuit when the current through it is too large.
The following fuses are marked with their maximum ratings.

When a current of 8A is used, which of the fuses will melt?

Q5   A heater normally uses 4A.
The manufacturer recommends a 5A fuse.

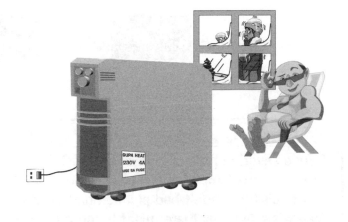

Describe and explain what would
happen if a 3A fuse was used.

Useful Circuits and Their Hazards

Q1　The circuit below shows a piece of fuse wire in series
with a cell, a bulb, a variable resistor and an ammeter.

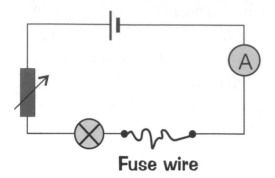

Fuse wire

a)　The resistance of the variable resistor is at maximum. The bulb is dim.

　　i)　Is the reading on the ammeter high or low?

　　ii)　Why is the bulb dim?

b)　The resistance of the variable resistor is slowly reduced.

　　i)　What happens to the reading on the ammeter?

　　ii)　Suddenly the fuse wire glows and melts.
　　　　Explain why this has happened?

　　iii)　Describe and explain what happens to the bulb.

Q2　If someone is not telling the truth they sweat slightly.
Wet skin has a lower resistance than dry skin.
The circuit for a lie detector is shown opposite.
The two probes are placed on the skin.

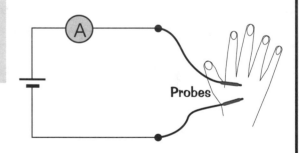

A pupil is connected to the
lie detector and asked questions.

The readings on the ammeter after two answers A and B are shown below.

A　6.3 MICROAMPS　　　B　0.4 MICROAMPS

Which answer is likely to be a lie? Explain your choice carefully.

If I see one more circuit question — I'll blow a fuse...

A fuse saved my Mum's life once. Well, kind of. She was cutting through the cable on an electric
lamp, but the lamp was still plugged in. Big flash, then there was a hole in the scissors. Mind you,
if the scissors hadn't had plastic handles, she probably would've been electrocuted anyway. So, a
fuse will blow, but there might be an instant when there's a big dangerous current flowing.

Types of Force

Q1 You can't see a force, but you can see the effects that a force has on an object. Name the three ways that a force can affect an object.

Q2 Copy and complete the sentences below.

Arrows are used in diagrams to show the .... and .... of forces.

A .... is an instrument used to measure forces.

This instrument measures forces in ....

Q3 Look at these magnets and then answer the questions below.

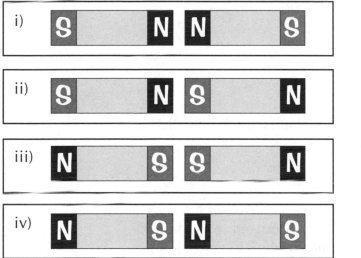

a) Copy out each diagram and add arrows to show the forces on the magnets.

b) For each part i) - iv), say whether the magnets are **attracted** or **repelled**.

Q4 Give a definition for each of the forces below.

    a) Upthrust

    b) Gravity

    c) Friction

Q5 Draw labelled diagrams to show an example of each type of force from question four.

I can't stop making these terrible jokes — it's just a force of habit...

Forces are everywhere, you just can't avoid them. They keep us standing up, they keep us afloat. Gravity is a fairly important one that stops us floating into space. In fact, the force is all around us, it binds us together, but beware the dark side. Hang on, ignore that last bit, I lapsed into Star Wars.

Density and Floating

Q1 Gravity and upthrust exist everywhere on earth, exerting a force on all objects. We know that gravity exists because we do not float off the surface of the earth. Copy the picture and draw the force arrows.

Q2 The same boy gets in the swimming pool.

a) What forces act upon him?

b) Draw a picture of him swimming at the surface with labelled arrows to show the four forces involved.

Q3 To work out if something will float or not you have to be able to calculate its density. To calculate density you need to be able to calculate volume. Calculate the volumes of the objects below.

a)

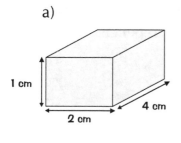

1 cm
2 cm
4 cm

b)

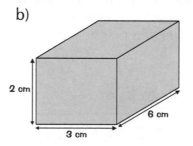

2 cm
3 cm
6 cm

c)

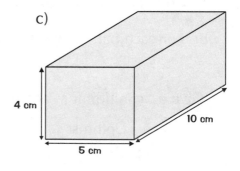

4 cm
5 cm
10 cm

d)

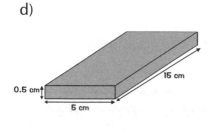

0.5 cm
5 cm
15 cm

e)

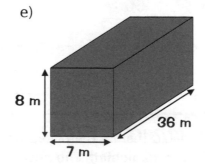

8 m
7 m
36 m

f)

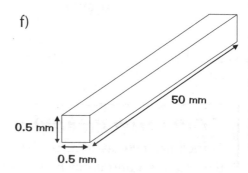

0.5 mm
0.5 mm
50 mm

Unit 7K — Forces and Their Effects

Density and Floating

Q1 An object will float in water if its density is less than the density of water.
Use these reminder boxes to help you answer the following questions.

$$\text{Density (g/cm}^3) = \frac{\text{Mass (g)}}{\text{Volume (cm}^3)}$$

The density of water is 1 g/cm^3

a) Calculate the density of the following objects.

i) 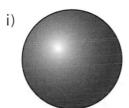 *mass = 100 g*
volume = 200 cm³

ii) 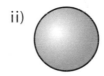 *mass = 100 g*
volume = 50 cm³

b) Which of the two objects (i or ii) will float in water?

Q2 Complete the sentence below with one of the phrases from the grey boxes.

When an object floats we can say that the forces are ....

| unbalanced | balanced | acting in the same direction |

| acting upwards | acting downwards |

Q3 Complete the table.

Object	Mass (g)	Volume (cm³)	Density (g/cm³)	Does it float in water?
a	200	100		
b	100	150		
c	60	200		
d	20	10		

OK, try one more time Northerners – "FLOAT" No, you're still saying flort*

It's getting a bit harder now. There's even some maths starting to appear. Gulp. Learn the formula for density and remember — an object floats if it's less dense than water (1 g/cm³). *kidding

Force Meters and Stretching

Q1 a) We can measure the weight of an object by using a force meter.
        What are the weights of the objects below?

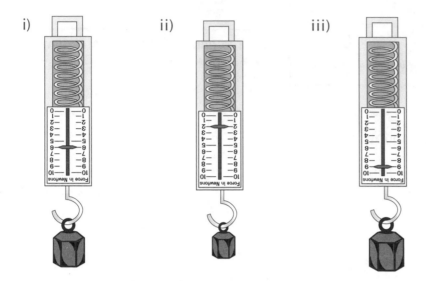

i)   ii)   iii)

Weights are
measured in newtons.

  b) Two forces can be seen in action in the diagrams above — gravity and upthrust.
      Are these forces balanced or unbalanced in the diagrams?

Q2 When materials are stretched and then allowed to return to the same shape, they
    are said to be elastic. A force meter (newton meter) has a spring that is elastic.

Weight	Distance Stretched
0.1 N	0.5 cm
0.3 N	1.5 cm
0.5 N	2.5 cm
0.7 N	3.5 cm
0.9 N	4.5 cm

  a) Using the data above plot a graph.

  b) Draw a line of best fit on the graph.

  c) If you place a weight of 0.4 N on the force meter, what would be the distance stretched?

  d) Predict what distance would be produced by a weight of 1.5 N

Mass and Weight

Q1 Mass is measured in kilograms (kg), weight is measured in newtons (N). Which of the following statements is correct?

a) A chicken has a weight of 2 kg and a mass of 20 N.

b) A chicken has a mass of 2 kg and a weight of 20 N.

Q2 Answer these questions about mass and weight.

a) Calculate the total weight of each team.

i)

Team name: The suits
Average mass: 70 kg

Team name: Fish
Average mass: 70 kg

ii)

Team name: The gap
Average mass: 40 kg

Team name: The geeks
Average mass: 60 kg

iii)

Team name: Pieman
Average mass: 50 kg

Team name: Army
Average mass: 50 kg

b) Make a table showing details for all the teams.

Include total weight, average mass, number of people and team names.

Newton came up with this one...

Or did he... Actually Robert Hooke (1635 - 1703) studied how things are elastic which led to the creation of the newton meter. Sir Isaac Newton got all the credit, the weasel.

Unit 7K — Forces and Their Effects

Friction

Q1 Copy out this paragraph and fill in the blanks using words from the grey box.

Friction is a .... that opposes ....

A .... surface gives .... of friction.

A .... surface gives .... friction. Friction

allows car tyres to .... the road surface — without this

grip the car wouldn't be able to move. .... use friction

to .... the car. If the brakes supply enough friction the

car will ....

> very little   grip   brakes   slippery   loads
>
> stop   grippy
>
> force   start   motion   slow down

Q2 The motorcyclist pictured below is travelling at a constant speed. Three forces — weight, friction and air resistance — act upon him.

a) Copy the motorcyclist and draw on the force arrows.

b) What happens to each of the following forces as he goes faster?

  i)   weight

  ii) friction

  iii) air resistance

Remember that forces can change direction, speed and shape.

Friction

Q1 Friction can be useful as well as unhelpful. Put the following statements into the correct part of the table.

a) Friction between the soles of your feet and the ground.

b) Friction in a car engine (eg. the pistons).

c) Friction between the brakes and the wheels.

d) Friction between a boat and the sea.

Useful	Unhelpful

Q2 Draw diagrams for a), c) and d) in question one. Include arrows and labels to show the direction of movement and friction. *[Don't do the engine. That'd be way too hard.]*

Q3 Copy out the paragraph below choosing the correct words where you have a choice.

A [lubricant / gas] is used to [reduce / increase] friction.

Lubricants are often [solids / liquids].

They are used to [dampen / smooth out] rough surfaces.

Q4 Answer these questions about friction.

a) Why do you put oil in car engines?

b) What would happen to the engine if you did not put oil in it?

c) Name two types of lubricants.

Q5 Which of these would produce more friction?

a) An ice cube sliding across a wooden table.

b) A wooden block sliding across a wooden table

Big Brother Thought of the Day: Avoid friction or it'll lead to your eviction...
Friction, what a teaser. Sometimes you want it, sometimes you don't.
A bit like brown sauce — great on chips, rubbish on meringue. Think on.

Stopping Distance

Q1   Copy out the sentence below filling in the blank.

The .... a vehicle travels, the greater the stopping distance.

Q2   Using the data below plot a graph.

Speed (miles per hour)	Stopping Distance (metres)
20	12
30	22
40	35
50	51
60	70
70	92

a) What happens to the stopping distance as the speed decreases?

b) Use your graph to work out the stopping distances at the following speeds:

  i)   25 miles per hour

  ii) 65 miles per hour

  iii) 45 miles per hour

Q3   The data above is the stopping distance for a vehicle travelling on a dry road.
What would happen to the stopping distances if the vehicle were travelling on a wet road?

Q4   Draw a distance/time graph for the following story.

a) A girl leaves home at 8am, she walks 1 km to her friend's house, she arrives at 8.15am.

b) She waits 5 mins for her friend.

c) They both leave at 8.20am. They walk to the bus stop 0.5 km away, it takes 5 mins.

d) They wait 5 mins for the bus.

e) They arrive at school at 8.45am. The bus travelled 10 km.

STOPping distance — hammer time...

Sorry if you're too young to remember this. (But if your teacher starts wearing baggy trousers, shuffling sideways like a crab and shouting "you can't touch this", don't be scared, they just do remember it.)

There's two things that affect stopping distance — friction (between tyres and the road) and speed.
The faster you go, the longer the stopping distance (no surprise there). When roads are wet, there's less friction. Things like ice and oil leave virtually no friction which makes them very dangerous.

Unit 7K — Forces and Their Effects

Orbits and Rotation

Q1 Rewrite the paragraph, filling in the gaps with words from the box:

> orbit   Earth   Moon   Sun   rotation

The .... travels in an .... round the .... One full circuit is one year. The .... also travels in an orbit round the Earth. It takes one month to complete this circuit. The .... of the Earth on its axis causes day and night.

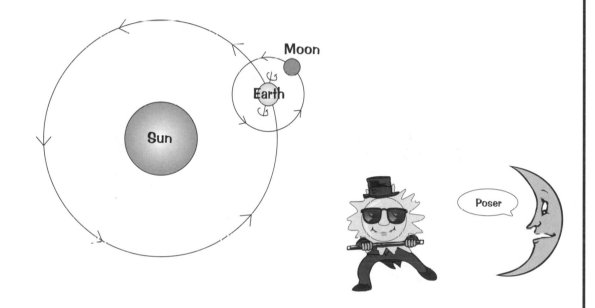

Q2 Using the diagram above, describe how the Earth's rotation causes day and night.

Q3 Explain why the Earth is split into different time zones.
(For example, parts of Australia are twelve hours ahead of the U.K.)

Q4 Why does the Sun appear to move across the sky during the day?
Draw a sketch to help explain it.

Q5 Explain how you know that the Earth is spherical, and not flat as people used to think.

How We See the Sun and Moon

Q1 Write down the main differences between a star (e.g. the Sun) and a planet (e.g. the Earth). See if you can find four.

Q2 Copy out the sentences below choosing the correct words from the box.

luminous	Moon	Sun	reflected

The Moon appears to us to be .... This is caused by light from the ....

being .... off the .... towards us.

Q3 The view of the Moon from the Earth shows a sequence of phases.

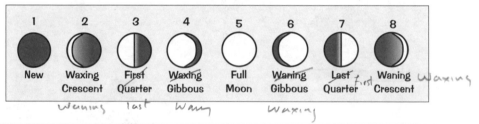

Copy out the diagram below and place a number in the circle to coincide with the phase at that point. I've done two for you.

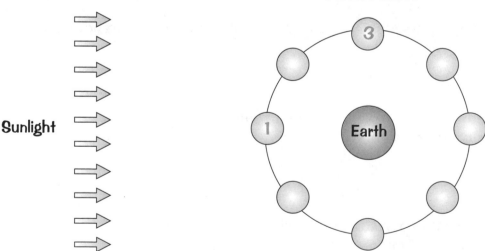

Q4 Explain the difference between a "full" Moon and a "new" Moon.

Q5 How long, to the nearest day, does it take for one orbit of the Moon round the Earth?

Eclipses of the Sun and Moon

Q1 The diagrams below show a lunar and a solar eclipse.
Fill in the missing words from this list (some occur more than once).

| Sun | Moon | Earth | Lunar Eclipse | Solar Eclipse |

....

....

....

....

....

....

....

....

....

not to scale

Q2 Describe in **simple terms** what happens during an eclipse of the Sun or Moon and explain the difference between the two.

Q3 The Moon's orbit is inclined slightly relative to the Earth's orbit. Explain what effect this has on eclipses. (Hint: does it make them more or less common?)

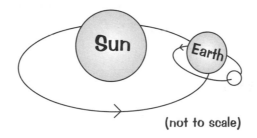

(not to scale)

not to scale

Once upon a time I was falling in love, now I'm only falling apart...

OK, I admit it — these pages probably won't make the Top 100 Easiest Pages Of All Time. If you're finding it difficult to understand, <u>learn</u> the answers to the questions. They're all simple facts you can find in a book. Once you know the facts, you can work backwards to <u>understand</u> it all.

The Causes of the Seasons

Seasonal effects arise on Earth because of the tilt of the Earth's axis (23.5°) combined with its orbit around the Sun.

Q1 Copy out the diagram and use these words to complete the labels.

| axis | day | night | sunlight |

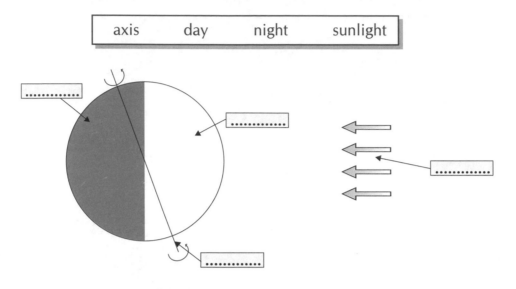

Q2 The Earth orbits the sun every 365 days. This is one year. During this time there are four seasons.

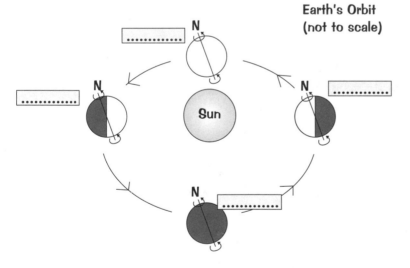

Earth's Orbit (not to scale)

(diagram not to scale)

a) Copy out the diagram.

b) Complete the labels to show the seasons (Spring, Summer, Autumn, Winter) for the Northern Hemisphere.

c) What is happening in the Southern Hemisphere at the same time?

d) Explain what would happen to the seasons if the axis of the Earth were not tilted.

For further info on the Four Seasons, look up Vivaldi...

Understanding how the tilt of the Earth's axis gives us seasons, is one of the trickiest things you're going to have to get your head round in Science. It's like this: Winter for us (in the Northern hemisphere) is when the top of the earth is furthest away from the Sun (because of the tilt). In our Summer, the top half of the Earth is closer to the Sun — we get long days and the Southern hemisphere gets shorter days and has its winter. Study the diagram until it all clicks.

Planets of the Solar System

Q1 Name each of the nine planets a) - i) orbiting the Sun as shown below.

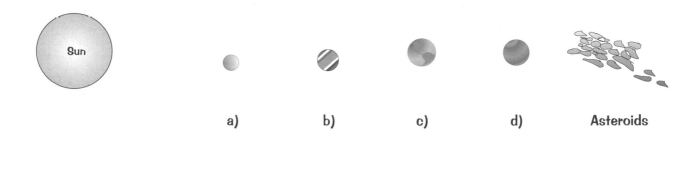

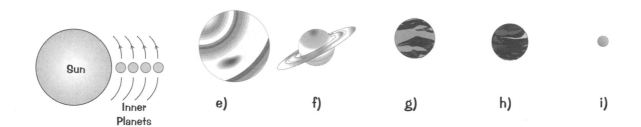

Q2 Showing the location of each planet on a diagram to the **correct scale** is difficult. Suggest another way of demonstrating the distance of the planets from the Sun, and the problems involved.

Q3 Copy and complete this passage about the orbits of the different planets by choosing the correct words from the grey box.

DAY   SUN   YEAR   SPIN   DIFFERENT

All the planets in our solar system orbit the ....

However the time taken for one orbit is .... for each planet.

The planets also .... at different speeds.

This means that the length of a .... and

a .... are different on each planet.

Space, the final frontier...

That last tip was a monster, so I'll keep this one short. Learn the nine planets, their order and the main facts about each one — that's all you're getting, sunshine.

Planets of the Solar System

Q1   The table below gives information about the planets in our solar system.

	PLANET	RELATIVE SIZE	RELATIVE MASS (Earth Masses)	MEAN DIST. FROM SUN (millions of km)	ORBIT TIME d=day, y=year
Inner Planets	Mercury	0.4	0.05	58	88d
	Venus	0.9	0.8	108	225d
	Earth	1.0	1.0	150	365d
	Mars	0.5	0.1	228	687d
Outer Planets	Jupiter	11.0	318.0	778	12y
	Saturn	9.4	95.0	1430	29y
	Uranus	4.0	15.0	2870	84y
	Neptune	3.8	17.0	4500	165y
	Pluto	0.2	0.003	5900	248y

a) Compare, using information from the table, the relative size
and mass of the four inner planets with the outer planets of the solar system.

b) Which planet is nearest to the Earth?

c) How many times further from the Sun is Pluto than Mercury?

d) Which planet is nearest in size to the Earth?

Q2   Imagine you are a space travel agent called Bob.   ⬅   *must be Bob — that's very important.*
Write a brief introduction to Mercury and Jupiter to tell travellers what they're like.

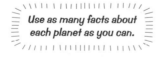

*Use as many facts about
each planet as you can.*

Q3   Within our solar system **only Earth**
is known to **support life**.
What conditions are necessary for life?

Q4   What evidence should we look for
in searching for life on other planets?

This rock might provide evidence that life once existed here.

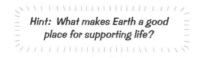

*Hint: What makes Earth a good
place for supporting life?*

Beyond the Solar System

Q1 Copy out the sentences below choosing the correct words from the list.

light	Planets	Sun	reflect	stars

We can see the .... and other .... because
they are sources of .... can only be
seen because they .... light.

Q2 Apart from the Sun, why can we only see the other stars at **night**?

Q3 Explain why the stars **appear** to **move** in the night sky.

Q4 Explain why we see different constellations of stars during a year.

Q5 The stars have been used for **navigation** for a very long time, especially at sea.

a) Copy and complete this paragraph about using the stars for navigation. Select the correct word from each pair.

> Stars can be used for navigation because they are in apparently [**fixed** / **moving**] positions compared to the [**Earth** / **Moon**] at particular times of the year. The [**pole star** / **Sun**] remains in the same position throughout the year (in the northern hemisphere). At sea there were no other useful navigation aids.

b) Why would the planets not be useful as a navigation aid?

Ooo — I feel a Starsailor song coming on...

Lie on your back in a field on a clear night and look at the stars. It'll make you, like, marvel at the enormity of the universe, man. But the only way to understand some of this tricky stuff is to practise these questions — so take off that tie-dye t-shirt, cut your hair and get working.

The Answers

Section 7A — Cells

Page 1

Q1 a) brain
   b) lungs
   c) heart
   d) liver
   e) kidneys
Q2 a) flower
   b) leaf
   c) stem
   d) roots
Q3 a) heart
   b) brain
   c) kidneys
   d) lungs
   e) small intenstine
Q4 a) leaves
   b) flowers
   c) root hairs
   d) stem
   e) roots

Page 2

Q1 A = The focusing knob
   B = Eyepiece
   C = The mirror
   D = Stage.
Q2 Cut the piece of epidermis with the scalpel and place it on the glass slide using the tweezers. Stain it with the iodine solution and cover with the cover slip.
Q3 The instructions should read:
   Put the slide on the stage.
   Check the slide is in the centre of the stage.
   Clip the slide onto the stage so it doesn't move around.
   Move round the three objective lenses to select the level of magnification.
   Adjust the mirror so that light shines up the microscope.
   Adjust the brightness.
   Look down the microscope.
   Adjust the focus to get a sharp image.

Page 3

Q1 a) nucleus
   b) cell membrane
   c) cytoplasm
   d) cell wall
   e) chloroplasts
   f) vacuole
Q2 a) true
   b) false
   c) true
   d) true
   e) false
   f) true
Q3

Part	Nucleus	Cell Membrane	Cell Wall	Chloroplasts
Animal	✓	✓	✗	✗
Plant	✓	✓	✓	✓

Q4 A matches to 3
   B matches to 4
   C matches to 1
   D matches to 2

Page 4

Q1 a) For movement.
   b) To digest its way to the ovum.
   c) chromosomes.
Q2 a) Large and bulky.
   b) A large food store.
Q3 a) carbon dioxide.
   b) light.
   c) chloroplasts.
Q4 a) Filter the air.
   b) mucus.
   c) dust and bacteria.
Q5 a) very big.
   b) water and minerals.

Q6 1. Tissue   C - A group of similar cells carrying out the same job
   2. Organ   B - A group of different tissues working together to carry out a common job
   3. Organ System   A - A group of organs carrying out a common function (job)
Q7 1. Tissue -   B. Muscular
   2. Organ - C. Heart
   3. Organ system - A. Digestive

Page 5

Q1 a) true
   b) false
   c) false
   d) true
   e) true
Q2 The missing words are:
   a) nucleus
   b) pollination
   c) half set
   d) specialised
   e) fertilisation
   f) seed
Q3 1. growth is **D an increase in mass**
   4. cell division starts with **E the nucleus dividing**
   3. new skin cells are produced by **C the division of existing skin cells**
   2. normal cell division **A involves the copying of genetic material**
   5. sperm cell production **B involves the manufacture of special cells with half the genetic information of normal cells plus a cute little tail**

Page 6

Q1 a) pollen grain
   b) female nucleus
   c) pollen tube
Q2 a) 1. Freda collects from a very

The Answers

healthy flower a large number of **D. Pollen grains to use in the experiment**

2. Fred adds 3 drops of each sugar solution onto a labelled **F. Cavity microscope slide**

3. They then add exactly 20 pollen grains to **G. Each labelled cavity slide**

4. They then cover each slide with a **H. Coverslip**

5. And then leave the slides for 30 minutes in an incubator set at a constant **A. Temperature of 28°C**

6. They then take each slide out quickly and **E. Count how many pollen grains have sprouted out of the twenty**

7. They then have some data on how well **C. Pollen grains sprout in different sugar concentrations**

8. Fred says I think we should draw a **B. Graph of the data and ponder it carefully**

b) They must come from the same plant so they are all identical & the only variable is sugar concentration

c) Anything less and the sample size would be too small for reliable data

d) Temperature is a variable that might affect sprouting of pollen tubes and so it must be controlled (kept constant)

Q3 A YES
    B NO
    C YES
    D YES

Section 7B — Reproduction

Page 7

Q1 The missing words are:
a) fertilisation
b) internal

Q2 a) Salmon
b) Any from: There is less chance of fertilisation. There is less chance of survival. They may get eaten. They may get washed away. No parental care.
c) Golden Eagles look after their young. Turtles do not.

Q3 a) False
b) True
c) True
d) False
e) False
f) True

Q4 a) The human
b) Nutrition (or milk/food).
c) They are hunted by lions for food.

Page 8

Q1 a) FEMALE
    A Ovary
    B Oviduct
    C Uterus
    D Uterus lining (or wall of uterus/womb)
    E Cervix
    MALE
    A Testis
    B Scrotum
    C Glands
    D Sperm tube
    E Penis
b) Ovary and testis should be circled.

Q2 a) Testes
b) Testes, sperm tube, penis (or urethra).
c) Vagina
d) So that there is more chance of one of them fertilising the egg.
e) Ovaries
f) The oviduct
g) Implantation — the fertilised egg (or embryo) embeds itself into the wall of the uterus.

Q3 The correct order is: C, A, D, B.

Page 9

Q1
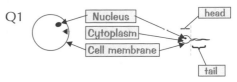

Q2 The description should match up:
Egg - is an enlarged cell with food reserves.
Nucleus - contains genetic instructions.
Cytoplasm - a jelly like substance that surrounds the nucleus.
Sperm - is streamlined and small in size.
Cell membrane - surrounds both the sperm and egg cells.

Q3 The missing words are:
nucleus, sex, fuse, external, genetic, identical twins, parents.

Q4

	Identical Twins	Non-identical Twins
Share the same genetic instructions	✓	
Their genetic instructions vary		✓
Are produced from one egg and one sperm	✓	
Are produced from two eggs and two sperms		✓
Must be the same sex	✓	
Can be different sexes		✓
Must be different sexes		

Page 10

Q1 a) Menstruation starts (period)
b) In preparation for a fertilised egg.
c) 14 days
d) The egg is released from the ovary and is fertilised in the oviduct.
e) 14 and 28
f) It will not be shed as it is needed to maintain the pregnancy
g) 30th January

Q2 a) Menstruation
b) Menstrual cycle
c) Implantation
d) Ovulation
e) Uterus

The Answers

Page 11

Q1 A: Zygote, B: embryo, C: fetus

Q2 a) A   Placenta
            Exchanges materials from
            mother's blood to fetus'
            blood and vice versa
        B   Umbilical cord
            Transports substances to
            and from fetus and
            placenta
        C   Amnion
            Bag that contains the
            amniotic fluid
        D   Cervix
            Muscle at the entrance to
            the uterus from the
            vagina
        E   Amniotic fluid
            Cushions and protects
            the fetus during
            pregnancy
        F   Uterus
            Organ where the fetus
            develops during
            pregnancy
        G   Vagina
            Baby leaves the mother's
            body through here (or
            sperm are deposited
            here)

    b) No. The uterus lining must
        be maintained during
        pregnancy.
    c) Morning sickness or enlarged
        nipples/breasts.
    d) One.

Q3 a) True
    b) False
    c) False
    d) True
    e) True
    f) False
    g) True

Page 12

Q1 The missing words are:

Nine	Birth	Contractions
Uterus	Amniotic	Cushioned
Cervix	Stronger	Closer
Vagina	Head	Umbilical cord
Blood	Afterbirth	

Q2 a) Any from; nutrition,
        antibodies passed
        from mother to baby, helps
        baby and mother to bond.
    b) Any reasonable answer, for
        example protection.

Page 13

Q1 a) Baby
    b) Child
    c) Adolescent
    d) Adult

Q2 a)

Height (cm) vs Age (years) graph showing Boys and Girls.

    b) Ages 12 to 14
    c) Ages 10 to 12
    d) 16 Years
    e) Girls are taller than boys until
        about 16 years. After this,
        boys tend to be
        taller. When fully developed
        boys are, on average, taller
        than girls. Girls develop
        quicker.

Page 14

Q1 Weight
    Head size
    Hand span
    Foot size

Q2 The missing words are:
    a) two
    b) identical
    c) skin

Q3 a) 146-150cm
    b) No
    c) 27cm
    d) Genetics, diet, illness,
        mother's diet/health during
        pregnancy.

Section 7C — Environment & Feeding Relationships

Page 15

Q1 The missing words are:
    a) habitat
    b) environment
    c) adapted
    d) adapted

Q2

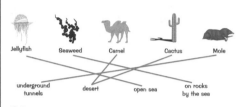

Jellyfish   Seaweed   Camel   Cactus   Mole

underground   desert   open sea   on rocks
tunnels   by the sea

Q3

LIVING THING:	FOUND WHERE:	WHY:
Polar bear	Swimming in icy cold water	It is hunting for prey (e.g. seals and fish)
Bat	In a cave during the day	It is resting
Cactus	In the desert	Because it is adapted to hot, dry conditions

Q4 The adaptations which help a
    badger feed at night in a
    woodland are:
    B Large claws for rooting around
    E Dark coloration,
        mainly, for camouflage
    F Very sensitive hearing

Page 16

Q1 The correct features are:
    A swallow: **migrates to warmer
    places for the winter**
    B Butterfly: **spends the winter as
    a pupa**
    C Tortoise **hibernates to survive
    over the winter**
    D Squirrel: **stores nuts
    underground**
    E Grizzly Bear: **grows a thick
    coat & stores extra fat for the
    winter** (OR **hibernates to
    survive over the winter**)

Q2 A Thermometer - 4. Temperature
    B Light Probe - 3. Light intensity
    C Rain gauge - 2. Rainfall levels
    D Meter measuring in decibels
                    - 1. Noise levels

Q3 The missing words are:

The Answers

a) petals
b) night
c) nocturnal
d) predators
e) salty

Q4 The missing words are:
1. temperature   2. sunlight
3. water   4. food

Page 17

Q1

Time	Light Level	What's happening?
Midnight	dark	It's 12 hours after noon.
4 am	dark	Nocturnal animals active
7 am	first light	Nocturnal animals are now hidden away.
12 noon	bright light	plants photsynthesising fastest.
4 pm	it is still light	Plant photosynthesis is slowing down.
8 pm	light fading	bats wake up and fly out of their roosts

Q2 a) Yes, but a larger sample would be better
b) Dark
c) After 2.5 minutes
d) A larger sample would give more reliable results
e) Lots of things such as temperature, humidity, age of the maggots, how well fed each maggot was, oxygen level in the container etc...
f) They prefer the dark to avoid being eaten by predators such as birds which won't be able to see them if they are in the dark

Page 18

Q1 A predator
B prey

Q2

Animal	Predator	Prey
Lion	✓	
Rabbit		✓
Earthworm		✓
Eagle	✓	

Q3

Feature	Predator	Prey
Sharp claws	✓	
Eyes on the side of the head for all round vision		✓
Excellent hearing and sense of smell	✓	✓
Excellent camouflage	✓	✓
Eyes forward	✓	

Q4 The missing words are:
a) producer
b) herbivore
c) carnivore
d) omnivore
e) herbivore vegetarian

Q5 A: food chain
B: food web

Page 19

Q1 The correct orders are:
a) Lettuce, Fiona (the vegetarian),
b) Grass, Daisy the cow, Phil (a human)
c) Seeds, Small bird, Oscar the Siamese cat
d) Corn, chicken, Sylvia (a human)
e) French lettuce, large juicy French snails, Jean (a nice Frenchman)
f) Pond Plant, Pond snail, Fish, Fred the Fisherman
g) Tiny plankton, Squid, Whale (Or plankton, whale, squid if it's a giant squid)
h) Oak leaves, Juicy Caterpillar, Robin, Large top carnivore bird
i) Leaves, Greenfly, Ladybirds, Bluetits, Hawk
j) Plant plankton, Animal plankton, krill (little Arctic shrimp-type creatures), Whale

Q2 a) is eaten by
b) energy
c) decrease
d) increase
e) Pond weed
f) Tadpole
g) Water Beetle
h) Pike
i) Tadpole
j) Water Beetle and Pike
k) Pike
l) Water Beetle and Pike
m) Tadpole and Water Beetle

Page 20

Q1 A: 3 - greenfly feed on roses
B: 4 - woodlice feed on rotting wood
C: 2 - spiders trap and eat houseflies

Q2 a) grass, wheat, blackberry, nettles, rose
b) plants
c) rabbit, field-mouse, aphid
d) fox, owl, ladybird, blue tit
e) 1 (the fox)
f) aphids increase, more aphids for ladybirds, more nettles and rose eaten
g) aphids increase, more for the blue tits, more nettles and roses eaten
h) less food for foxes so they eat more field-mice and/or more owls
i) increase in field-mouse population, more wheat and blackberries eaten

Page 21

Q1 a) True
b) True
c) False
d) True

Q2

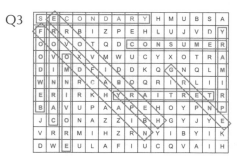

Q3

The Answers

Section 7D — Variation and Classification

Page 22

Q1 a) 4
   b) 6
   c) 30
   d) 22

Q2 a) Yes. There is a general pattern that the taller people tend to have the longest feet
   b) Quite strongly
   c) D - tall with small feet, J - short with big feet
   d) Collect more data / larger sample

Q3 There is no pattern - the data does not support Peter's idea.

Q4 a)

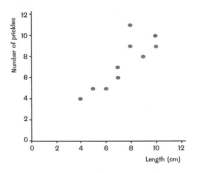

   b) The data suggests that Beth is correct but more leaves would have to be studied to be more certain.

Page 23

Q1 The missing words are: different, inherit, environmental, colour of petals, height, water, light.

Q2 a) i) Green eyes, round chin, large pointed nose
      ii) Stick out ears
   b) i) Hair colour — unless it's dyed
      ii) Curly hair, square chin, brown eyes
   c) Clare - missing teeth, long hair (allow hair colour)
      Billy - black eye, hair style
   d) Yes. Unless he shaves it off.

Page 24

Q1

Characteristic	A	B	C
Teeth	Large rear teeth	Large sharp	None
Body covering	Fur	Shell/scales	Feathers
Legs	4	6	2
Wings	No	No	Yes

Q2

Characteristic	A	B	C
Diet	Herbivore	Omnivore	Carnivore
Gives birth to	Live young	Eggs	Eggs
Feeds young	Milk	No	Meat
Mating	Partner for life	Different	Partner for life
Hibernates	Yes	No	No

Page 25

Q1 a) One fin or two fins
   b) 4
   c) A, D, G, H and B, C, E, F
   d) i) Stripes
      ii) Wave - A, D and F
          Spots - B and G

Q2 a) A - dung beetle
      B - peat beetle
      C - mud beetle
      D - rock beetle
   b) Black head, spots on abdomen

Page 26

Q1 A - Vertebrates B - Mammals
   C - Amphibians D - Reptiles

Q2 Whether or not it has a backbone.

Q3 a) Bear, snake, lizard, bird, fish, toad, brontosaurus.
   b) Ant, bee, snail, spider, worm.
   c) Bear. Fur. Gives birth to live young which are fed milk
   d) Toad. Moist skin. Lays eggs in water.
   e) Ant, bee, spider.

Section 7E — Acids and Alkalis

Page 27

Q1 The missing words are: sour-tasting, vinegar, lemon juice, diluting, water, aspirin.

Q2 Five acids are: Tomato sauce, orange juice, aspirin, vitamin-c tablets and Coca-Cola.

Q3 The three symbols are: A (corrosive), D (irritant), and E (harmful).

Q4 **Hazardous** Battery acid, Drain cleaner, Toilet cleaner, Bleach. **Non-hazardous** Lime juice, Mayonnaise, Vitamin-C, Baking soda, Toothpaste, Pickle.

Page 28

Q1 Any suitable poster. Should include things like: **goggles, gloves, lab. coat, funnel, lots of water to dilute any spills.**

Q2 The correct article should read: A tanker overturned in Haztown town centre today spilling its ten tonne load of strong acid.
A year 7 student passing by read the hazard warning on the tanker and rang the fire service.
The fire service washed the acid away with lots of water.
This diluted the acid.
A spokesperson for the fire service said: 'Acid is less dangerous when it is diluted with water.

Q3 Any suitable instructions. Should include things like: **goggles, mask, gloves, wash affected area with water.** Perhaps: **well ventilated, seek medical advice if serious.**

Page 29

Q1 The missing words are: colour, acids, indicators, blackcurrant

Q2 Acid
   Alkali
   Acid
   Alkali
   Alkali
   Acid

Q3 a) red
   b) red
   c) blue
   d) red
   e) blue

Q4 a) **A**cid
   b) **L**itmus
   c) **K**itten
   d) **A**lkalis
   e) **L**emon
   f) **I**ndicators

Q5 a) Two from lemon, lemonade, vinegar
   b) Red cabbage, blackcurrants
   c) Two from drain cleaner

The Answers

(sodium hydroxide), washing up liquid, soap
d) Two from hydrochloric acid, sulphuric acid, nitric acid

Page 30

Q1 The correct words are:
red, blue, green.
Q2 a) pH
b) acids
c) neutral
d) alkalis
Q3 a) pH7
b) pH14
c) pH5
d) pH9
e) pH1
Q4 a) rainwater and lemon juice
b) water and blood
c) oven cleaner, washing up liquid and sodium hydroxide
d) car battery acid (sulfuric acid) and stomach acid (hydrochloric acid)
Q5 Any sensible answer, could include: wear goggles; wear protective gloves.

Page 31

Q1 The missing words are:
alkali, 14, acid, neutral, neutralised, lower, acidic.
Q2 The correct sentences are:
b, c, e, f, g
Q3 a) acid
b) nothing
c) alkali
Q4 The correct table is B.

Page 32

Q1 The missing words are:
hydrochloric, alkaline, neutralise, acid
Q2 b and c are the most important.
Q3 The correct order is
a, e, g, d, c, b, f
Q4 Any sensible answers, eg: use the same amount of acid each time; try to crush up each tablet so that the bits of powder are roughly the same size.
Q5 **Two from:**
The cost of the powder
What the powder tastes like
Whether the powder is poisonous

or not
Whether the powder is corrosive or not
How quickly the powder neutralises the acid.

Section 7F — Simple Chemical Reactions

Page 33

Q1 a) temperature rise
b) bubbles of gas
c) smell
d) colour change
e) flame
Q2

Chemical changes	Physical changes
Burning toast under a grill	Turning water into ice in the freezer
Boiling an egg	Salt disappearing as it is stirred into a beaker of water
Igniting a Bunsen burner	
Green copper carbonate powder turning to black copper oxide when heated strongly	Water droplets forming on a kitchen window near a kettle of boiling water

Q3 A chemical change makes new substances and is (usually) irreversible. A physical change does not make new products and is reversible.
Q4 a) You can see bubbles forming.
b) Chemical change.

Page 34

Q1 a) 1 - bubbles of gas
2 - metal disappears / gets smaller
b) Put a lighted splint at the mouth of the test tube of gas. If it's hydrogen, the gas pops.
Q2 a) i) copper, lead or other relatively unreactive metal
ii) magnesium or other reactive metal
b) hydrogen
Q3 The missing words are:
zinc, hydrogen, reaction, disappears, corrosive

Page 35

Q1 limestone, marble, baking powder, chalk
Q2 a) labels are:
A = acid,
B = limestone chips,
C = limewater,

D = carbon dioxide gas
b) the limewater turns cloudy/ milky
Q3 The true statements are:
a, c, d and f.
The rest are false.

Page 36

Q1 The missing words are:
chemical reaction, oxygen, air, oxide, irreversible.
Q2 magnesium + oxygen ⟶ **magnesium oxide**
iron + **oxygen** ⟶ iron oxide
zinc + oxygen ⟶ **zinc oxide**
sulphur + oxygen ⟶ sulphur dioxide
Q3 a) Any 4 of: Pupils 2m from demo, don't look directly at flame, teacher and pupils wear safety glasses, teacher wears gloves, use tongs, don't touch residue after reaction.
b) magnesium burns more brightly in pure oxygen, reaction is over more quickly in pure oxygen.

Page 37

Q1 a) i) water
ii) to turn the water vapour into liquid / condense the water vapour
b) i) carbon dioxide
ii) it would go a milky colour
Q2 replacement words are:
a) (any fuel)
b) carbon
c) burning
d) methane
e) water
Q3 methane + o**xygen** ⟶ **carbon dioxide** + **water** + energy

Page 38

Q1 a) it ran out of oxygen
b) it had a (limited) supply of oxygen in the jar
c) it rose / went up
d) because the water took the place of the used up oxygen
e) oxygen
Q2 a) as the (volume of the) beakers

The Answers

got bigger, the time it took for the candle to go out got longer.

b) this happens because the bigger the beaker, the more oxygen is available to keep the candle alight.

c) about 110 - 120 seconds

Section 7G — Solids, Liquids and Gases

Page 39

Q1 a) solid
  b) liquid
  c) gas
  d) solid
  e) solid
  f) liquid
  g) solid
  h) liquid
  i) gas
  j) solid

Q2 The correct sentences are:
A gold particle has a greater mass than an aluminium particle.
The gold particles are closer together than the aluminium particles.

Q3 The correct words are:
can't, close together, far apart, closer together.

Q4 a)

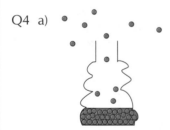

b) The person who is close to the bottle smells it first because the perfume particles do not have to go very far. It takes longer for the particles to reach the person who is further away.

Page 40

Q1 The missing words are:
slowly, faster, particles, further, big.

Q2 A matches 1
B matches 3
C matches 2

Q3 With 10g the particles are very close together and the forces between the particles are very strong
With 160 g the particles are slightly further apart and the forces between the particles are still strong enough to hold them together
With 200g the particles in the middle of the wire are so far apart that the wire snaps because the forces between these particles are now too weak to hold them together

Page 41

Q1 The missing words are:
evidence, observations, explain, theories, experiments, change.

Q2 a) Matthew - because he goes to the gym often so is probably thin enough and strong enough to get through the skylight. It is probably not Jason because he is too fat to fit through the skylight and is afraid of heights. It is probably not Aidan because his leg is in plaster.

  b) Aidan can't swim; Jason was eating a pasty.

Q3 a) Z
  b) W
  c) X
  d) Y

Page 42

Q1

Property	Solids	Liquids	Gases
Volume	Definite volume	Definite volume	No definite volume -fill their container
Shape	Definite shape	Match shape of container	Match shape of container
Density	High density	Medium density	Very low density
Ease of Flow	Don't flow	Flow easily	Flow easily

Q2 a) e
  c) solid
  d) liquid

Q3 a) Solid. Each grain of sand has a fixed shape and volume and cannot be compressed. Each grain cannot flow.

  b) Solid. Before you start chewing the gum, it has a fixed shape and volume. It does not flow.

  c) Small bits of solid mixed with a liquid. Like a liquid, it can flow and change its shape. You can filter out small pieces of solid.

  d) Liquid with small bits of solid in it. It can flow and change its shape. The small bits of solid have fixed shapes and volumes.

  e) Liquid when in the container - it flows, takes the shape of its container and has a fixed volume.
Liquid in the air - small droplets travel from the container to your hair.
Solid when it has dried on your hair - its shape is now fixed.

Page 43

Q1 a) solid
  b) liquid
  c) gas

Q2

ice   liquid water   steam

Q3

	Solids	Liquids	Gases
How close are the particles?	Very close	Very close	Far apart
How do the particles move?	Vibrate on the spot	Move past each other in all directions	Move fast in all directions

Q4 The true statements are:
Strong forces hold the particles together in solids.
Solid particles are arranged in a regular pattern.
Quite strong forces hold the particles together in liquids.
It is difficult to compress liquids.
Gases expand to fill their container.
Gas particles collide often with each other.

The Answers

Q5 The particles should be spread across the bottom of the container; the top of the liquid should be horizontal; the particles should touch each other.

Page 44

Q1 The missing words are:
lots, spread, particles, few, diffusion.

Q2 Air particles move around all the time.
Air particles bump into dust particles.
When an air particle bumps into a dust particle the dust particle moves off in a different direction.

Q3
grey particles

Q4 The correct words are:
water, faster, hot, darker.

Q5 The ink particles spread out from where there are lots of them to where there are fewer of them.
It takes a few hours for the black particles to be spread out evenly in the water.

Section 7H — Solutions

Page 45

Q1 a) a single substance, not a mixture
b) more than one substance which can be separated using physical means.
c) Anything sensible.
c) The mixtures are: a, c, d.

Q2 a) Soluble
b) Insoluble
c) Anything sensible like common salt or sugar.
d) Anything sensible like sand, gravel, glass.

Q3 a) The colour is blue so the copper sulfate must still be there
b) Evaporate the water off

Q4 a) soluble
b) insoluble
c) solute
d) solution

Q5 By filtering.

Q6 Evaporate a sample until all the liquid has gone. If there's any solid remaining, the liquid was a mixture.

Page 46

Q1 To see how much salt there is in a sample of rock salt

Q2 Apparatus such as: balance, beaker, glass rod, filter funnel, filter paper, evaporating dish, heat mat, tripod, Bunsen burner, gauze, spatula.

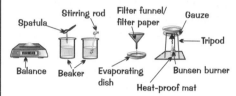

Q3 a) Use a balance
b) Place it in water
c) Filter it
d) Evaporate to half volume or so and leave to crystallise out
e) Could scrape salt out of evaporation dish and find its mass, but some could be left in the dish. Better way would be to find the mass of the evaporating dish before it was used, then take this away from the final mass of the dish + salt.

Q4 3g

Q5 a) 30%
b) Repeat experiment to validate results, might weigh filter paper then dry the sand and rock and reweigh to check its mass plus mass of salt = 10 g

Page 47

Q1 a) To accurately weigh the salt
b) 115 g
c) Nothing disappeared — salt and water were both there. So Mass of the mixture = Total mass of material

d) The salt is dissolved and so will pass through the holes of the filter paper.

Q2 a) Salt
b) It had turned into a gas / evaporated
c) evaporation
d) 15.00 g
e) In dissolving material does not disappear, mass is conserved

Q3 Third diagram should have particles of salt and water intermingled, particles should be labelled.

Page 48

Q1 a) To heat up the water and make it evaporate / boil off
b) Cools down the water vapour and turns it back to liquid water
c) The blue dyes have been left behind in the conical flask
d) Check it boils at 100°C or use cobalt chloride paper

Q2 Correct order is
g), f), b), e), d), a), c)

Q3 a) Water is heated by the sun and evaporates. The water vapour hits the plastic sheet which is cooler and condenses to water. The sheet is angled so the water runs down the sheet and into the can.
b) It has been separated from the seawater mixture. (In reality it may have some salty taste as it is not the best way of distilling).
c) The water is heated the most when the sun shines brightly so the separation is faster.

Page 49

Q1 The correct sentences are:
a), d), e)

Q2 a) = chromatogram
b) = beaker
c) = solvent
d) = wick

Q3 Set up apparatus as in diagram above, the spot of original material can be made by soaking a smartie in a few drops of water

The Answers

for a few minutes. Drop this in the middle of the chromatogram and use water as the solvent

Q4 a) Use of science and technology to solve crimes

b) Analysis blood samples / identification of drugs / anything sensible

Q5 Drawings and explanation to show how the solvent particles give the solute particles a piggyback through the chromatogram and then dump them at a certain place.

Page 50

Q1 The correct statements are a), c), e).

Q2 Add 0.5 g samples to the water at a time and stir. Count how many samples are added. When no more will dissolve you have the amount which will dissolve (i.e. minus 0.5 g added).

Q3 a) 21 g of potassium nitrate will dissolve in 100 g of water at 10°C

b) 10.5 g

c) 42 g

d) You wouldn't want to add more than the maximum amount which is soluble, as it would be a waste.

e) Not as useful as soluble ones as plant take in the nutrients dissolved in water through their roots.

Q4 The correct description is d).

Page 51

Q1 a) B

b) A

c) As the temperature increases so does the solubility

d) Because the solubility is temperature dependent

e) A

Q2 a) It increases with temperature

b) 36.2 g

c) 36.8 g/100g water

d) roughly 39 g/100g water

e) 3.62 g

f) roughly 0.75 g

Section 71 — Energy Resources

Page 52

Q1 a) Oil or Gas,

b) Gas (or petrol, kerosene, paraffin)

c) Diesel or Coal,

d) Charcoal or Wood .

Q2 The missing words are:

a) burned, move.

b) burned, light.

c) burned, heat.

D) burned, move.

Q3 They are all types of energy.

Q4 FUEL + **OXYGEN** ⟶ **ENERGY**

Q5 The correct statements are:

a) give out a lot of heat

c) are easy to light

d) burn steadily

i) burn with a clean flame

j) are easy to transport.

Page 53

Q1 The fossil fuels are:

c) Natural gas

d) Coal

g) Oil

Q2 Oil and natural gas are mostly made of dead animals.

Q3 In the sea.

Q4 The correct order is: a, d, b, e, c, f.

Q5 Fossil fuels take millions of years to form, they are not replaced as fast as we use them.

Q6 a) depends on your age and what year you are reading this!

b) fewer cars, electric cars/other transport, more coal fired power stations, other reasonable answers.

c) Supplies of coal will be used at a faster rate.

d) Answers could include ways of saving energy, e.g. insulating homes, thermostats, showers instead of baths etc
Use alternative sources of

energy, for heating, transport, examples may be given, electric cars, trams etc, cars with smaller engines.

Page 54

Q1 The missing words are: renewable, can, fast.

Q2 a) Wind turbine or aerogenerator- uses wind

b) Solar panel - uses solar energy or sunlight

c) geothermal power station - geothermal energy

d) hydroelectric power station - uses energy of falling water,

e) bonfire/wood fire - uses biomass

Q3 Energy from waves.

Page 55

Q1 The missing words are:

a) wind, electricity.

b) water, turbine, generator, electricity

c) cold, hot, steam, generator

d) electricity.

Q2

Energy Resource	Advantage	Disadvantage
Solar	No air pollution	Sun doesn't always shine
Wind	Renewable resource	Turbines are large, noisy and costly
Geothermal	Renewable resource	Few areas in the world are suitable
Hydroelectric	Clean, no air pollution	Habitats of wild animals destroyed
Biomass	Renewable resource	Large areas of land needed

Other sensible advantages/ disadvantages are OK.

Page 56

Q1 Any appropriate activity, e.g. flying, running, swimming etc.

Q2 The missing words are: energy, food, resource, energy, joules.

Q3 1,000 J

Q4 a) baked beans

b) lettuce

c) 1069 kJ

Q5 a) The amount of activity undertaken, the more strenuous the activity the more energy required.

b) He would lose weight.

c) He would gain weight.

Q6 The energy value of the meal should = 4,000 kJ. Various combinations of foods listed possible.

The Answers

Section 7J — Electrical Circuits

Page 57

Q1
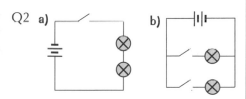

SYMBOL	NAME
———	Wire
	SWITCH
⊝ OR ⊗	Bulb
Ⓥ	Voltmeter
Ⓐ	AMMETER
⊦⊦⊦⊦	Battery made of three cells

Q2 a)   b)
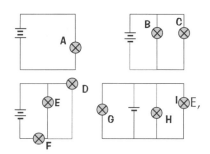

Q3 The missing words are:
a) complete
b) closed
c) can't
d) negative
e) energy

Page 58

Q1 The bulbs that will light are:
A, E, F

Q2 The switches that MUST be closed are:
A   1,2,6 or 1,3,4,6 or 1,5,4,6
B   1,3,4,6 or 1,5,4,6
C   1,2,6
D   1,5,4,6
E   1,5,4,6
F   1,3,4,6
G   1,2,6 or 1,3,4,6 or 1,5,4,6

Page 59

Q1 The missing words are:
current, amps, series
Q2 Y = 4A, Z = 4A.

Q3 a) FALSE.
As more bulbs are added the current DECREASES.
b) TRUE.
c) FALSE:
Putting more bulbs in the circuit INCREASES the total resistance
d) TRUE.

Page 60

Q1 A = 3V, B = 3V, C = 4.5V, D = 6V.
Q2 a) 2
b) 8 and 9
c) 1 and 4
Q3 a) High
b) The bulb dims because the current through decreases.

Page 61

Q1 M = 2A, N = 2A, P = 4A, Q = 6A
Q2 The altered paragraph should read:
"The **cell** pushes the **current** around the circuit. It is easy to push the **current** through the **wires**. The **bulb** offers more resistance. Turning the **switch** off stops the flow of **current** throughout the whole circuit. To push more **current** you could use a higher **voltage cell**. To have less **current** flowing in the circuit put another **bulb** in series"

Page 62

Q1 a) The missing words are:
parallel, more, resistance, water.
b)

Q2 a) G = 8A, H = 12A.
b) Because there is less resistance on the top branch, only 1 bulb.

Page 63

Q1 The missing words are:
230, lower, dangerous, wet, resistance, large, kill.

Q2 There is likely to be moisture in a bathroom and you might touch the socket with wet hands. The water might allow a current to flow from the mains wires through you.
Q3 This socket only supplies 12V. The voltage is not high enough to push a dangerous current through you.
Q4 The 3A and 5A fuses will melt.
Q5 During normal operation the 3A fuse would melt and the heater would stop working.

Page 64

Q1 a) i)   Low
ii) Because the current through it is low
b) i)   Increases
ii) The current was high enough to melt the fuse wire
iii) The bulb goes out because the circuit has been broken
Q2 Answer A is the lie as the person would have slightly sweatier skin which has a lower resistance and allows a larger current to flow.

Section 7K — Forces and Their Effects

Page 65

Q1 1 - Change in speed
2 - Change in direction
3 - Change in shape
Q2 The missing words are:
size, direction, forcemeter or newton meter, Newtons

Q3 a)
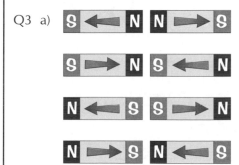

The Answers

b) i) Repulsion
ii) Attraction
iii) Repulsion
iv) Attraction

Q4 a) Any upwards force on an object in a fluid (such as air).

b) The force of attraction between two bodies (for example, the force acting downwards on a mass pulling it towards the centre of the earth.)

c) Friction is the force which tries to stop objects sliding past each other.

Q5 a)

b)
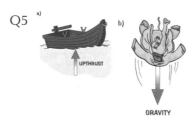

c)
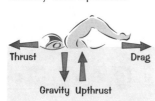

Page 66

Q1
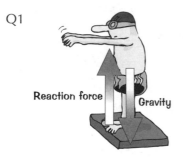

Q2 a) Gravity and upthrust.

b)

Q3 a) 8 cm³   b) 36 cm³
c) 200 cm³   d) 37.5 cm³
e) 2016 m³   f) 12.5 mm³

Page 67

Q1 a) i) 0.5 g/cm³
ii) 2 g/cm³

b) large ball, i)

Q2 Balanced.

Q3

Object	Mass (g)	Volume (cm³)	Density (g/cm³)	Does it float in water?
a	200	100	2	No
b	100	150	0.67	Yes
c	60	200	0.3	Yes
d	20	10	2	No

Page 68

Q1 a) i) 6N
ii) 2N
iii) 9N

b) balanced

Q2 a), b)
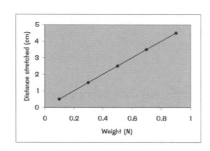

c) 2cm
d) 7.5cm

Page 69

Q1 Statement b is correct

Q2 a) i) 3500n, 4200n
ii) 2400n, 2400n
iii) 1500n, 1500n

b)

Team name	Average mass (kg)	Number on team	Total Weight (N)
The Suits	70	5	3500
The Gap	40	6	2400
Fish	70	6	4200
The Geeks	60	4	2400
Pieman	50	3	1500
Army	50	3	1500

Page 70

Q1 The missing words are:
force, motion, grippy, loads, slippery, very little, grip, brakes, slow down, stop.

Q2 a)
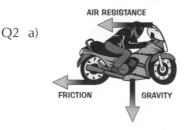

b) i) weight remains constant
ii) friction increases
iii) air resistance increases

Page 71

Q1

Useful	Unhelpful
Friction between the soles of your feet and the ground	Friction in a car engine
Friction between the brakes and the wheels	Friction between a boat and the sea

Q2 a)
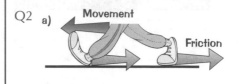

c)
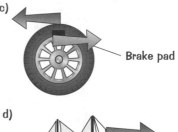

d)

Q3 The missing words are: lubricant, reduce, liquids, smooth out.

Q4 a) To enable to moving parts to move more freely or reduce friction

b) Friction and heat would build up causing the engine parts to fail.

c) Oil, water or any other substance that reduces friction eg. washing up liquid

Q5 Situation b would create more friction.

Page 72

Q1 The missing word is **faster**.

Q2

The Answers

a) The stopping distance decreases
b) i)   17 m
   ii)   81 m
   iii) 43 m
Q3 Stopping distances would increase for wet roads.

Q4

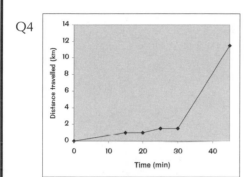

Section 7L — The Solar System and Beyond

Page 73

Q1 The missing words are:
Earth, orbit, Sun, Moon, rotation.
Q2 The Earth rotates on its axis once every 24 hours. The part facing the Sun at any time is experiencing daytime, while the unlit part is in darkness, and experiencing night time.
Q3 Different time zones allow all parts of the world to be synchronised with the 24-hour day. eg, midday in Britain will occur 12 hours before midday on the other side of the Earth.
Q4 The Earth's rotation causes the Sun to rise and set. The curve traced out by the Sun varies with season and latitude.
Q5 1) Pictures from rockets and satellites etc.
   2) The curvature of the horizon of the sea.
   3) Day and night caused by the Earth's rotation.
   4) Navigation - if the Earth was flat ships would fall off the edge!

Page 74

Q1 The main difference are:
   1) Stars emit light — planets reflect light.
   2) Stars are much bigger than planets.
   3) Planets orbit stars.
   4) Planets move over a period of time, whereas stars stay fixed.
Q2 The missing words are: luminous, Sun, reflected, Moon
Q3 The numbers 1-8 should be written in order, clockwise, starting with 1 at 9 o'clock position.
Q4 A full Moon occurs when the Moon is on the opposite side of the Earth from the Sun and it appears as a fully illuminated disc. At New Moon the Moon is not visible because it is between the Earth and the Sun and the side facing Earth is not illuminated.
Q5 28 days.

Page 75

Q1 Reading from left to right, the missing words are:
Sun, Moon, Earth, Solar Eclipse
Sun, Earth, Moon, Lunar Eclipse
Q2 An eclipse of the Sun occurs when the Moon is directly between the Sun and the Earth and blocks out all light across the eclipse track. The Earth being positioned between the Sun and the Moon causes an eclipse of the Moon as the Earth's shadow falls on the Moon.
Q3 The inclination of the Moon's orbit means that eclipses are relatively unusual events. If the Moon's orbit were not inclined, solar and lunar eclipses would take place every month.

Page 76

Q1 (from left to right, top to bottom)
Night, day, sunlight, axis.
Q2 b) Anticlockwise, starting from top: autumn, winter, spring, summer.
   c) spring, summer, autumn, winter.
      (i.e. the opposite season)
   d) If the Earth had no axial tilt, there would be no seasons. The polar areas would each receive the least amount of heat and light. Heat and light would increase towards the equator, and day and night would be equal everywhere.

Page 77

Q1 a) Mercury
   b) Venus
   c) Earth
   d) Mars
   e) Jupiter
   f) Saturn
   g) Uranus
   h) Neptune
   i) Pluto.
Q2 The Solar System could be modelled using spheres of various sizes.
The inner planets would be straightforward to model, both in terms of size and distance from the Sun. The outer planets would be more difficult as the distances are so great.
Q3 The missing words are:

The Answers

Sun, different, spin, day, year.

Page 78

Q1 a) The inner planets are all relatively small and of similar size. They also have a similar mass. The outer planets are much larger than the inner planets (The mass of Jupiter is over three hundred times that of the Earth). They are obviously at much greater distances from the Sun.

b) Venus

c) 102

d) Venus

Q2 Mercury

The planet closest to the Sun. Small, dense and with no atmosphere. Very hot on sunlit side (480°C). Very cold on dark side (-180°C). Orbits the Sun in 88 Earth days. Rotates on its axis once every 58 days. The surface is very much like our Moon. It has no satellites.

Jupiter

The largest planet in the solar system and the fifth planet from the Sun. Thirteen times further from the Sun than Mercury. Composed primarily of hydrogen and helium. Its mass is nearly 6000 times that of Mercury. Orbits the Sun once every 12 years. Rotates on its axis in just 10 hours. A prominent feature is the Great Red Spot. It has sixteen satellites.

Q3 The three essentials for life to exist are: the correct temperature (not too hot and not too cold), the presence of oxygen for respiration, and water.

Q4 Looking for evidence of life on other planets involves searching for the three essentials (Q3) or for life itself. On Mars (the planet with the best chance of supporting life forms in the Solar System), clues have been sought to suggest that life at one time existed there. Examples of this are fossils, and very simple microscopic life forms.

Page 79

Q1 The missing words are: Sun, stars, light, planets, reflect.

Q2 The sky is too bright from sunlight to allow the stars to be viewed in daylight. The exception to this is during a total eclipse of the Sun.

Q3 The stars appear to move because of the rotation of the Earth on its axis.

Q4 We see different constellations during the course of the year because of the Earth's journey through its orbit round the Sun.

Q5 a) The correct words are: fixed, Earth, pole star

b) The position of the planets is never fixed and so they could not be used for navigation purposes.